To Loretta

God Bless you

Wendell K

cLv

Werner Gitt

Did God
Use Evolution?

clv

Christliche
Literatur-Verbreitung e.V.
Postfach 11 01 35 · 33661 Bielefeld

The Author, Prof Dr-Ing Werner Gitt: He was born in Raineck/East Prussia in 1937. In 1963 he enrolled at the "Technische Hochschule Hannover" (Technical University of Hanover/Germany) and in 1968 he completed his studies as "Diplom-Ingenieur". Thereafter he worked as assistant at the Institute of Control Engineering at the "Technische Hochschule Aachen". Following two years of research work, he received his doctorate in Engineering summa cum laude together with the prestigious "Borchers Medal" of the Technical University of Aachen. In 1971 Werner Gitt started his career at the German Federal Institute of Physics and Technology (Physikalisch-Technische Bundesanstalt "PTB"), Brunswick, as Head of Data Processing. In 1978 he was promoted to Director and Professor at the PTB. He has written numerous scientific papers in the field of information science, as well as many others concerned with numerical mathematics and control engineering. Besides his scientific publications he is well known as author of several popular books, some of which have been translated into Bulgarian, Czech, English, Finnish, French, Hungarian, Italian, Polish, Russian. In 1966 Werner Gitt married his wife Marion. They have two children, Carsten and Rona.

1st English edition 1993

© Copyright of the German edition:
Werner Gitt, "Schuf Gott durch Evolution?"
1988 by Hänssler-Verlag, Neuhausen-Stuttgart

© Copyright of the English edition:
1993 by CLV · Christliche Literatur-Verbreitung e.V.
Postfach 11 01 35 · D-33661 Bielefeld

Distribution for South Africa:
R. Steinberg, c/o SIM SA
P.O. Box 129, Mondeor 2110 RSA

Translation to English: Prof Dr Jaap Kies
Correction: Marianne Rothe
Cover: Dieter Otten
Typography: CLV
Printed in Germany: by Ebner Ulm

ISBN 3-89397-725-2

Contents

1. Introduction   7

2. Scientific Questions   9
    2.1   The Principles of Science Theory   9
    2.2   The Basic Assumptions of Evolution   13
    2.3   The Basic Assumptions of Creationism   17
    2.4   The Basic Assumptions of Theistic Evolution   24
    2.5   Some Consequences   25

3. Anthropological Observations   27
    3.1   The Origin of Man (OB1)   27
    3.2   The Origin of Human Language (OB2)   29
    3.3   The Origin of the Sexes (OB3)   33
    3.4   The Origin of Marriage (OB4)   34
    3.5   The Origin of Death (OB5)   36
    3.6   The Origin of Religions (OB6)   44
    3.7   The so-called "Fundamental Law of
          Biogenetics" (OB7)   46
    3.8   The Essential Nature of Man (OB8)   48
    3.9   Human Behaviour (OB9)   51

4. Astronomical Observations   53
    4.1   The Origin of the Universe (OB10)   53
    4.2   The Future of the Universe (OB11)   57
    4.3   The Centre of the Universe (OB12)   59

5. Biological Observations   61
    5.1   The First Life on Earth (OB13)   61
    5.2   "Each According to its Kind" (OB14)   63
    5.3   Animal Nourishment (OB15)   66
    5.4   Differences Between Human Life and
          Animal Life (OB16)   67

6. Observations on Information Science   71
    6.1 What is Information?
         The View of Informatics (OB17)   71
    6.2 What is Information?
         The Biblical View (OB18)   74
    6.3 What is Life? The Evolutionary View   76
    6.4 What is Life? The Informational View (OB19) 78
    6.5 What is Life? The Biblical View (OB20)   81
    6.6 The Origin of Biological Information
         and of Life   82

7. Progressive Evolution or Completed Creation?   87

8. The Consequences of Theistic Evolution   89
    8.1 Danger No 1: Denial of Central Biblical
                       Teachings   89
    8.2 Danger No 2: Misrepresentation of the
                       Nature of God   92
    8.3 Danger No 3: Loss of the Key for
                       Finding God   94
    8.4 Danger No 4: God's Incarnation becomes
                       Incidental   95
    8.5 Danger No 5: Relativation of Jesus's Work
                       of Redemption   97
    8.6 Danger No 6: God becomes a God
                       of the Gaps   98
    8.7 Danger No 7: Loss of Biblical Chronology   100
    8.8 Danger No 8: Misrepresentation of Reality 102
    8.9 Danger No 9: Loss of Creation Concepts   105
    8.10 Danger No 10: Missing the Purpose   107

References   111

Index of Authors   119

Abbreviations of the Books of the Bible   123

Glossary: Explanation of Terms   125

1. Introduction

1. *The present situation and readership:* The theory of evolution is currently so widely established that it could be described as the all-inclusive and even the only philosophy of the twentieth century.

The idea of self-organisation from the simple to the more complex, has been commonly appropriated – even in disciplines foreign to biological evolution. The development of computers is often falsely referred to as the "evolution of computers", even though the current high-performance computers are the result of intensive research by many brilliant minds. They have been planned, constructed and produced on purpose and are clearly not the result of an evolutionary process.

Theology, too, was affected; evolutionary ideas have even been carried into biblical exegesis.

We will show below why evolutionistic thought is completely foreign to the Bible. This book is aimed predominantly at Christian readers who might be inclined to accept some version of theistic evolution. Over and above that, the book is set out in such a way that sceptical readers may also be guided to some decision.

2. *Modus operandi:* The basic assumptions of science are discussed in a separate chapter. This should enable the reader to recognise which basic assumptions he automatically accepts when he decides for or against creation or evolution.

Use of the term "the THEORY of evolution" is intentionally avoided, because, according to the standards of science theory, evolution is a philosophical doctrine, and not a scientific theory. For the same reason we do

7

not refer to creation THEORY, but to the biblical doctrine of creation. Creation research concerns itself with deducing models from physical reality, which are based on fundamental biblical statements. A total of twenty objections (OB1 to OB20) against theistic evolution is discussed in this book. In addition to valid criticisms of evolution, the alternative, creation, is increasingly expounded more clearly in recent literature, such as [B4, E2, G3, G5, G7, G8, G10, G11, J2, S3, S4, S5]. This book also refers repeatedly to this very sustainable alternative.

As far as possible, the objections are discussed along the following lines:

1. The dictates of evolution

2. Scientific objections against these dictums

3. Biblical refutations of evolutionary assumptions

The author is an information scientist, but the discussions on information concepts in Chapter 6 should be readily understood by the layman. In the last chapter scientific and biblical objections against evolution culminate in the exposition of ten dangers inherent in theistic evolution. Many quotations expose the anti-biblical nature of such a viewpoint.

3. *Acknowledgments:* The original manuscript was scrutinised by *Prof Dr Horst W Beck, Dr Reinhard Junker* and *Dr Jan Kaminski*. I am very grateful for all their suggestions and additions.

I am grateful to *Prof Jaap Kies* who was able to devote his valuable time to the translation of this book. A special note of appreciation is due to *Marianne Rothe* who edited the translation.

Werner Gitt

2. Scientific Questions

2.1 The Principles of Science Theory

Science theory concerns itself with the possibilities and the limits of scientific knowledge. The basic assumptions of a theory are discussed, applicable methods for increasing man's knowledge are explained, and, eventually, the validity of scientific pronouncements is reviewed and evaluated. Some basic principles (P1 – P11) are enunciated below:

P1: *Every theory requires basic assumptions* (a priori postulates) which cannot be proved. These presuppositions are not observable, but are of a metaphysical nature (Greek: *metà tá physiká* = above physics, i.e. not based on observation). Such assumptions are recognised by convention. As *W Stegmüller* [S7 p 33] affirms: "One need not push knowledge aside to make place for belief. Rather, one must already believe something before you can speak of knowledge and science."

P2: *The basic assumptions are arbitrary postulates* which appear plausible to the author. According to the theoreticist, *Karl R. Popper*, the fundamental principles of a theoretical system may be compared to the conclusions reached by a jury in a criminal case. The verdict is the basis for the practical processes which comprise the joint deductions made from the statutes of criminal law. The verdict, however, need not be the final judgment; it can be repealed or revised by an appropriate process.

Popper explains [P5 p 110-111]: "The analogy between this procedure and that by which we decide basic statements is clear. It throws light, for example, upon their relativity, and the way in which they depend upon questions raised by the theory. In the case of the trial by jury, it would be clearly impossible to *apply* the 'theory' unless there is first a verdict arrived at by decision; yet the verdict has to be found in a procedure that conforms to, and thus applies, part of the general legal code. The case is analogous to that of basic statements. Their acceptance is part of the application of a theoretical system; and it is only this application which makes any further applications of the theoretical system possible. The empirical basis of objective science has thus nothing 'absolute' about it. Science does not rest upon rock. The bold structure of its theories rises, as it were, above a swamp. It is like a building erected on piles. The piles are driven down from above into the swamp, but not down to any natural or 'given' base; and when we cease our attempts to drive our piles into a deeper layer, it is not because we have reached firm ground. We simply stop when we are satisfied that they are firm enough to carry the structure, at least for the time being."

P3: *The initial postulates must be mutually consistent and should be free from inherent contradictions.*

P4: *When competing theories contradict one another* (apart from errors in measurement and observations), the fault is not to be sought in the facts, but in differences in the basic postulates.

P5: *The basic postulates may be objectively criticised and even rejected.* The quality of the basic assumptions of two competing systems determines the practical success of the ensuing theories.

P6: *If a theory is successful, it does not follow that it is correct.* "Consequently, theories are never empirically verifiable" (*K Popper* [P5 p 17]). According to *Popper* consistency is not a truth criterion, but, on the other hand, inconsistency does falsify a theory. No all-inclusive theorem, like "All swans are white", can ever be verified, not even by end-less experimentation. Theories can only survive, and are only provisionally valid, for as long as they are not shown to be false by empirical reality (when a single black swan is found), and subsequently replaced by a new, better theory.

P7: *An empirical scientific system must allow experimentation.* *Popper* proposes the falsifiability of a theory as criterion, not its verifiability. This means that it must be possible to negate a theory by means of methodical experimentation; the logical structure of the system must allow for negation [P5 p 41]. "It must be possible for an empirical scientific system to be refuted by experience." One single contra-dictory experimental or observational result is therefore sufficient to discard a theory in its present form. A theory is good exactly when it can very readily be refuted. If it then survives any barrage of cross-fire attacks, it proves its merit. It becomes a "natural law" only after very many substantiations.

The physical law of the conservation of energy is a prime example of a very easily refutable theory, because one single unexpected experimental result will be sufficient to disprove it. This has never happened, and this law is ge-nerally accepted. Furthermore, it is a fundamentally im-portant and useful theorem in all the exact and technical sciences. Any theory which insures itself against falsifica-tion, and which is therefore inviolable, is scientifically tri-vial and untenable. It only provides a philosophical view-point.

Consequently, *Popper* defines the "real sciences" as follo-ws [P5 p 314]:

"In so far as a scientific statement speaks about reality, it must be falsifiable: and in so far as it is not falsifiable, it does not speak about reality."

P8: *It is necessary to distinguish between structural and exact sciences* on the one hand, and historical-interpretive sciences on the other hand, because of fundamental differences. This aspect is discussed fully in [P6 p 112 ff].

P9: *In contrast to the theorems of the structural sciences (mathematics, informatics), no theorems of the experimental sciences can be proved;* they are only more, or less, strongly established: "All knowledge is only inferential. The various conjectures or hypotheses are intuitive inferences. They are weeded out by experience, bitter experiences, and they are replaced by better conjectures: This is the only end result of experimentation in science" (*K R Popper* [P5 p 565]).

Popper also states that sure knowledge is denied us. Our knowledge is a guessing game, a network of hypotheses, a fabric of conjectures [P5 p 278]: "*We do not know: we can only guess.* And our guesses are guided by the unscientific, the metaphysical faith in laws, in regularities which we can uncover, discover."

P10: *A theory can only be advanced if an example that can be practically duplicated (by experiment or observation), is available.* The theorems derived from the theory must be testable, or rejectable by falsification. The acceptance of a theory depends on its repeatability.

P11: *A theory must allow predictions.* The correctness of such predictions is a prerequisite for the acceptability of a theory.

In what follows, we will discuss the essential theoretical principles of the doctrines of creation and of evolution, and of theistic evolution. It will be patently clear that the two views are so strongly divergent, that reconciliation is totally impossible. This calls for a decision. In Chapters 3 to 6 we will show that the observations and facts of the exact sciences can be convincingly explained by the creation model.

2.2 The Basis Assumptions of Evolution

The following assumptions (E1 to E12) are fundamental principles of the doctrine of evolution but, unfortunately, they very seldom if ever appear explicitly in evolutionary writings, although evolutionary findings depend fundamentally on them.

They are usually taken for granted and are often only implied, so that the reader finds it difficult to determine whether the statements made about evolution are based on observational data or are the basic assumptions dressed up as conclusions.

E1: *The basic principle, evolution, is taken for granted. F M Wuketits*, an evolution theorist, writes [W5 p 11]: "We presuppose the essential correctness of biological evolution, yes, we assume that evolution is universally valid."

Siewing defines biological evolution as follows [S6 p 171]: "The essence of the theory of evolution is contained in the statement that all systematic categories are eventually related; therefore all known organisms are descendants of one common ancestor."

E2: *Evolution is a universal principle:* "The principle of development not only holds for life on earth; it extends much further. It is quite clearly the most widely valid principle imaginable, because it encompasses the entire universe … All of reality around us is characterised by a history of self-development. Biological evolution is only part of this universal process" (*Hoimar von Ditfurth* [D3 p 22]).

E3a: *One should not drag in a Creator* (or synonyms such as Designer, planning Spirit, or "Demiurge"). *Ernest Kahane*, a French molecular biologist, formulates it as follows (quoted in [S5 p 16]): "It is absurd and absolutely preposterous to believe that a living cell could come into existence by itself; but, notwithstanding, I do believe it, because I cannot imagine anything else." Assumption E3b follows as a consequence of E3a:

E3b: *This world, including all living organisms, is based exclusively on matter and materialistic principles.* It follows that the origin of life can only be found in matter. One can therefore exclude the possibility of a spiritual Author for matter itself and for all life forms.

"This view frees us from the difficulty of assuming that at some stage during the course of the development of our earth, after animal life had started, something immaterial or psychical, nobody knows from where, stepped in and caused various effects in brains and brain capacities" (*B Rensch* [R1 p 235]).

E4: *Matter is taken for granted.* The law of the conservation of energy together with *Einstein's* equivalence of matter and energy $E = m \cdot c^2$ states that the sum total of all energy and all matter in our universe is constant. There is thus no scientific explanation for the origin of matter and energy, and it is therefore necessary to assume that all the energy must have existed before the supposed big bang.

E5: *As far as scientific laws are concerned, there is no difference between the origin of the earth and of all life,* and their subsequent development (the principle of uniformity).

The mechanisms of the processes through which the earth and all life on earth originated, were subject to the same laws that govern the present observable reality (compare assumption C3 of creationism).

E6: *Evolution relies on processes that allow increases in organisation from the simple to the more complex, from non-life to life, from lower to higher life forms.*

14

These processes are described as the "self-organisation of matter". The so-called evolutionary factors are mentioned as cause (see E7). In the vein of E6 *B Rensch* defines the evolution of the cosmos up to man as follows [R1 p 235]: "Evolution manifests itself as a continuous progression from the origin of the solar system and the earth, through the assemblage of the first elements of life, followed by true forms of life, and increasingly higher developed groups of animals, leading up to man."

E7: *The following factors are assumed as the driving forces of evolution: Mutation, selection, isolation, and mixing.* Chance and necessity, long time epochs, ecological changes, and death are additional indispensable factors which are included in the "actual" evolutionary factors.

E7a: *"Mutation and selection are the driving forces of evolution" (K Lorenz).*

Remark: If there were only one single example (experiment or observation) of the origin of a new kind of organism or a new structure, then E7a would have been a derived theory. The mechanisms, mutation and selection, do occur, and the appearance of a new kind would imply new genetic information. But because of the lack of any evidence of new genetic information, E7a remains an assumption.

E7b: *Death is an undisputed essential factor in evolution.* Biologist *H Mohr* states [M2 p 12]: "If there were no death, then no life would have existed ... There is no other way around this axiom of evolutionary theory."

E8: *There is no plan in evolution, neither is there any purpose.* No causes should be postulated for the purposefulness perceived in organic life, because that would imply a Creator: "It is not necessary to assume a mysterious guiding principle for the purposefulness observed in the structure and life of all organisms, ... neither was a wise

15

Creator necessary for their origin" (*B Rensch* [R1 p 66]). Other quotations point in the same direction: "No causes can operate from the future; therefore there can be no pre-determined evolutionary purposes" (*H v. Ditfurth*).

E9: *There are no definite beginning and end points on the time axis.* Anybody can therefore have as much time as he likes for the process of evolution. With a universe oscillating from one big bang to the next, E9 becomes patently obvious [W2 p 16]: "Many cosmologists embrace the model of an oscillating universe on philosophical grounds, mainly because it glibly evades the issue of Genesis." Because of the unlimited available time in the future, *Carsten Bresch* hopefully expects further evolutionary "hits" [B7 p 291]: "When unlimited time is available, then sometime, somewhere, one individual will progress to the next step when he 'throws a six'."

E10: *The present is the key to the past.* This means that present-day observational data may be extrapolated as far back in time as one wishes. Examples: The present annual rate of erosion of the Grand Canyon is 0.15 mm. This leads to an age of 10 million years. The current measured rate of expansion of the universe based on the *Hubble* constant, places the time of the big bang at 18 thousand million years in the past. Astronomer *O Heckmann* critisises this "remarkable sport" and describes it as calculating with "reckless abandon" [H4 p 90].

E11: *There was a smooth transition from non-life to life.* The continuous development from simple atoms and molecules up to man is regarded as a smooth change-over from one example to the next: "The smooth conversion (from non-life to life) is a postulate of a reductionistic explanation" (*B-O Küppers* [K4 p 200]).

E12: *Evolution will persist in the distant future:* "When this planet becomes a 'monon', evolution will enter its intellectual phase. We can only guess about its future course ... The direction is illustrated in the development from chaos to an intellectual intergalactic supermind; each one of us is a small part of it all" (*Carsten Bresch* [B7 p 265, 293]).

Note: It is significant that the enunciations of the doctrine of evolution do not comprise the final conclusions resulting from measurements and observations, but more often than not, they describe the system of basic assumptions. As regards models of the origin of things and life, only theories which fit the concepts of evolution, are allowed (the science of evolutionary knowledge!). Sir *Arthur Keith* summarises the above as follows: "Evolution is unproven and unprovable. We believe it however, because the only alternative is an act of creation by a God, and that is unthinkable."

The evolutionary understanding of the Bible: There is no personal God. Consequently the Bible has been written BY humans FOR humans, as any other piece of literature. The Bible reflects the thoughts of the time and place of its writing, and thus has no claim to the truth, neither can it be regarded as authoritative.

2.3   The Basic Assumptions of Creationism

Theories and models of the various creation disciplines are based on the following presuppositions. Assumptions E1 and C1, E2 and C2, ... E12 and C12 deal with the same topics; their contents, however, are diametrically opposed. The basic assumptions clearly show that these two sets of principles are incompatible.

C1: *The basic principle of creation is taken for granted.* An understanding of the original creation can only be obtained through a biblical "temper of mind". Biblical revelations are the key for understanding this world. The Bible is the basic, irreplaceable source of information. It is a fact of creation that we may not extrapolate the currently valid natural laws into the six days of creation. Our present experiences do not allow us to really evaluate something that has just been created.

Examples: All adults were children. But Adam could not have been created as a baby; he was a grown man. He never was a child, and it does not make sense to extrapolate a number of years into his life, just because our present experiences require that every adult should have been a child. Similarly all the stars were immediately visible in spite of immense distances. Trees were not made as seedlings; they were fully grown and complete. Neither did the birds first have to hatch from their eggs and eventually grow up. The old question of "which was first – the hen or the egg?" has a clear and unambiguous biblical answer.

C2: *Creation is a universal principle,* i e the entire universe and all life on earth originated at creation. According to John 1:1 & 3 creation encompasses everything from the microcosm to the macrocosm and from inanimate matter to man: "In the beginning was the Word, and the Word was with God, and the Word was God. Through him all things were made; without him nothing was made that has been made."

C3: *The Creator exists.* He is the God of the Bible. The Bible begins with the affirmation "In the beginning God created the heavens and the earth", and this is clearly an important basic assumption as defined by us. God is not there to fill the as yet unexplainable gaps in natural phenomena, but He is the Primal Cause of ALL things, whether or not we already understand them scientifically. If we should relegate to the Creator only those matters which are not (yet) explainable, then everything which has already been explained, may be used to "prove" the non-existence of

God. Then, as scientific knowledge accumulates, God is increasingly "explained away" (see Chapter 8.6).

C4: *The matter of the entire universe has been created without the use of previously existing matter.* This basic principle is formulated in Hebrews 11:3: "By faith we understand that the universe was formed at God's command, so that what is seen was not made out of what was visible."

C5: *There is a fundamental difference between the creation of the world and all living organisms on the one hand, and the subsequent processes.* Natural laws derive from our experiences with matter which consistently repeat themselves; the present creation functions according to these laws in every detail. They were established at creation and provide the limits within which expected outcomes are guaranteed and can even be calculated beforehand (e.g. the law of gravity, and the laws governing chemical reactions). These limits demarcate both possible events as in technological achievements, as well as impossible events (e.g. stones falling upwards, and "perpetual motion" machines functioning without energy being supplied). The physical processes within living organisms are also subject to these limits.

C6: *God's creative activities cannot be explained in terms of natural laws, neither are they subject to the above limits.* Creation is a singular event by which the present natural laws came into existence. Concerning these creative acts, one can only look so far across this "event horizon" as God reveals in His Word. That which God has revealed in Holy Scripture is therefore fundamental and irrefutable information which cannot be obtained otherwise.

Comment: According to the well-known law of the conservation of energy, energy cannot be created nor can it be destroyed in this universe. This fact illuminates basic assumption C6. The origin of the energy presently in the universe cannot be described in terms of known physical laws, because creation occurred outside the currently valid laws. Evolutionary presupposition E6 is contradicted by C6.

Analogy: The origin of the Bible can be seen as analogous to the creation of the universe. If creation cannot be explained in terms of natural laws, neither can the origin of God's Word be explained by scientific methods like history, text criticisms, or archaeology. According to Isaiah 55:8-9 the acts of God concerning the establishment of the Bible is outside our field of understanding, therefore we can only understand it as far as it is revealed in God's Word.

C7: *The following factors or causes of creation are mentioned many times in the Bible:*

- by the Word of God: Ps 33:6; John 1:1-4; Hebr 11:3
- by the power of God: Jer 10:12
- by God's wisdom: Ps 104:24; Prov 3:19; Col 2:3
- according to the will of God: Gen 1:26; Rev 4:11
- by the Son of God: John 1:1-4 & 10; Col 1:15-17; Hebr 1:2b
- according to the character of Jesus: Matt 11:29; John 10:11; John 14:27
- out of nothing: Hebr 11:3
- instantaneously: Ps 33:6

These factors were in operation during the six days of creation. They are not subject to natural laws and can therefore only be comprehended by faith (Hebr 11:3).

C8: *Purposes require a Designer.* Aspects of creation clearly point to the Creator (Rom 1:19-20). They bear witness to the wisdom (genius, intelligence, richness of ideas; Col 2:3) and omnipotence (Ps 19:2) of the Creator; but they do not disclose His other characteristics (like love, grace, goodness) and functions (Saviour, Redeemer, Comforter) which are essential for our faith in Him.

In the vein of C8 it has been reasoned as follows: "Let us imagine that some astronauts discovered a golden calf on the moon, or that deep sea explorers stumble on a statue of Venus. Even if they bore the inscription 'sculpsit evolutio' (shaped by evolution), I regard it as more likely that intelligent beings had produced them, than assuming that chance and necessity were the cause" (*L Oeing-Hanhoff* [O1 p 63]).

Comment: It is highly significant that the remarkable genius observed in nature is explained (especially in living organisms). One should not replace the biblical conclusions leading from creation to the Creator, with contrived philosophical "proofs" of God's existence – "For although they knew God" (Rom 1:21a).

Knowledge of God and Christ is only obtained through the Word of God in the Bible: As proclaimed by the spoken and the written word (Rom 10:17; Rev 1:3) and the personal witness of believers (Acts 1:8).

C9: *There is a definite beginning point of time, as set out in Genesis 1:1.* Time and matter came into existence at creation, and they will also have a definite end (Rev 10:6b). The age of the universe is tied up with the existence of human generations (biblical genealogies), and is definitely not of the order of millions or billions of years.

C10: *The past is the key to the present.* This is exactly the inverse of the evolutionary presupposition E8. The present can only be understood in the light of three crucial past events: Creation, man's sin, and the Noahic flood. Three secondary basic theorems can be deduced:

C10a: *Death is the result of the sin of the first human couple* (Gen 2:17; Gen 3:17-19; Rom 5:12, 14; Rom 6:23; 1 Cor 15:21).

21

C10b: *All life forms were adversely affected by man's sin* (Rom 8:20, 22). The destructive biological structures (e.g. bacteria which cause diseases, parasites, death-dealing mechanisms of snakes, spiders, and predatory plants and animals, and tribulations resulting from "thorns and thistles") cannot be explained except as a result of sin. The generally observed impermanence of things has also been caused by sin.

C10c: *The present geological structures of the earth's crust cannot be explained without recourse to Noah's flood.*

C11: *There is a clear difference between living organisms and non-living matter.* Matter and energy are necessary fundamental qualities of all life, but they do not distinguish living systems from non-living systems. One of the central characteristics of all living creatures is the inherent information required for all life processes and the genetic information required for procreation. Information is an essential aspect of all life forms. In the extreme case, submicroscopic viroids are no more than bearers of information. On the other hand, even very complex organic compounds like proteins are not alive, because they do not contain encoded information. It should be obvious that information distinguishes between living and inanimate substances. *Pasteur's* statement that life can only come from life (omne vivum ex vivo), can thus be expressed as follows: Information must have a source.

C12: *The creation of living organisms (original kinds) is completed.* As described in Genesis 1, all original living types ("each according to its kind") were created during the six days of creation. All later changes (e.g. races) are merely variations of the previously created original kinds.

Creation research comprises the following: (Note: Creation research refers to the investigation of that which has already been created; God's creative acts themselves are hidden from us (see assumption C6).)

1. *All scientifically available facts are used.* As far as they involve measurements and observations, facts are processed by means of currently available scientific instruments.

2. *Biblical statements are not the object of creation research, rather, they are the point of departure.* It is not the intention to prove the validity of Bible, but to show that the facts of nature can be much more readily explained by means of premises based on the Bible than by using an evolutionary approach.

3. *All theories based on the assumption of evolution, are evaluated critically.* When considering scientific results (facts and meanings), there is a distinct difference between the purely factual aspects of data, and conclusions based on the doctrine of evolution. Theories formulated in creation research, are equally subject to critical scrutiny and eventual improvement. Only explicit biblical statements are not questioned.

4. *How the Bible is understood:* Human authors wrote as inspired by God's Holy Spirit (2 Peter 1:20, 21; 2 Tim 3:16). God supervised the exact words used originally, even to the point of the actual choice of correct idiomatic expressions, without circumventing the personalities of the writers. In this way the Bible carries the seal of truth, and all its pronouncements are authoritative – whether they deal with questions of faith and salvation, questions of daily life, or matters of scientific importance [G6 p 44-45]. The Bible is the ONLY revelation authorised by God, apart from personal guidance in daily matters. God abhors all other purported revelations (e.g. occultism, meditation and the founding of cults and religions), see Deuteronomy 4:2; Proverbs 30:6; 1 Corinthians 4:6; Revelation 22:18-19. Further aspects of the interpretation of the Bible are discussed in Chapter 8.1.

2.4   The Basic Assumptions of Theistic Evolution

Evolutionary assumptions E1, E2, E5, E6, E7, E9, E10, E11 and E12 are directly applicable to "theistic evolution". Three additional theorems distinguish it from "plain" evolution. There is an unbridgeable chasm between theistic evolution and the biblical doctrine of creation.

T1: *God used evolution as a means of creating.*

T2: *The Bible contains no usable or relevant ideas which can be applied in present-day science.*

T3: *Evolutionistic pronouncements have priority over biblical statements.* The Bible must be reinterpreted when and wherever it contradicts the present evolutionary world-view. *J Illies* states [I5]: "Using a correction factor of 1 to 365 000, brings us to two thousand million years, which is much closer to the truth."

The theistic approach to understanding the Bible: The existence of God is assumed. But He is not at all the form-giving and inspiring Author of the Scriptures. Rather, the Bible is regarded as the product of historical influences; the writers reflected their own circumstances and the contemporary world view. *A Läpple* uses this view when he describes the Bible as being conceived by human endeavours [L1 p 42]:

> "They regarded the earth as a round, flat disk. It is the centre of the universe, floating on the primeval ocean – the waters below the earth … The solid firmament above spans the terrestrial disk, with the sun, moon and stars fixed to it like lamps."

The Bible is regarded as a collection of documents which partially contains God's Word, amongst others. According to this viewpoint various creation myths and different traditions are recognised. The real contents are only revealed when these cultural and historical shells are removed. The Bible thus contains no authoritative, binding truths, but must be freshly interpreted and corrected for every era and in every situation.

2.5 Some Consequences

1. FROM THE PHILOSOPHY OF SCIENCE: No absolute knowledge is available. The idea of autonomous human reason has been shown to be invalid according to present-day theories of science. All of man's science has a preliminary character, as *Popper* maintained [P5 p 280-281]: "The old scientific ideal of *episteme* – of absolutely certain, demonstrable knowledge – has proved to be an idol. The demand for scientific objectivity makes it inevitable that every scientific statement must remain *tentative for ever* ... for it is not his *possession* of knowledge, of irrefutable truth, that makes the man of science, but his persistent and recklessly critical *quest* for truth."

   Bible-believing Christians ought to know that there are no scientific-philosophical objections today which prohibit the use of the Bible for explaining the facts of nature (creation science). The fundamental concepts of the Bible are God's revelation, a source which far surpasses human reason and comprises a solid rock foundation. A scientist who is predisposed to evolution (see evolutionary assumption E1), can present his models as hypotheses only, which – according to *Popper* – stand on unstable marshy ground.

2. FROM CREATION RESEARCH: Questions of origin can only be answered when an a priori revelation is available (see assumption C6). We agree with *W Pauli*, winner of the Nobel prize in physics, who said that all scientific methods fail when questions of origin are involved. Biblical enunciations thus have a wider range of applicability than scientific statements. The present author has discussed this question fully in [G2 p 21-24].

25

When we creation scientists describe nature convincingly and consistently, our model will not be acceptable to some people, because it implies the living God's existence and assumes the truth of the entire Bible. This is not surprising, for science is completely secularised, and theology is largely liberalised. *Popper* holds the plausible view that a competing theory is best vindicated if it survives the most stringent tests. If this criterion is applied to the acceptance of creationism, its rapid growth should be significant.

3. FROM THEISTIC EVOLUTION: Proponents of theistic evolution relegate the Bible to a subordinate role. When the Bible is quoted, the purpose usually is to read other meanings into the Scriptures, namely those required by evolution. Many contemporary scientists and believers have unfortunately been led astray to a false understanding of Holy Scripture.

3. Anthropological Observations

3.1 The Origin of Man (OB1)

EVOLUTION: In his book "The descent of man" *Charles Darwin* concludes as follows: The most meaningful result in this book, that man descended from a lowly organised life form, will be a stumbling block for many. I regret that. But there can hardly be any doubts about our descent from savages. According to current evolutionary teachings man's genealogy not only reaches back into the animal kingdom, but right back to simple inorganic molecules: Primeval soup → primitive slime → primeval cell; single-celled organisms then became multi-cellular: → worms → fishes → amphibians → reptiles → mammals → primitive primates → apes → ape-men → hominids → man.

Nobel prize winner *Jacques Monod* regards our existence as a necessary consequence of a game of chance [M3 p 137]: "The universe was not pregnant with life nor the biosphere with man. Our number came up in the Monte Carlo game. Is it surprising that, like the person who has just made a million at the casino, we should feel strange and a little unreal?"

Rupert Riedl also emphasises the purposelessness of human existence [R2 p 221]: "Man was not planned. In fact, the causal chain of events leading up to man was coincidental. But the results are in the last place necessities … The alternations between necessary chance and accidental necessity has now moved completely inwards: at present the required prejudgements originate inside the central nervous system as preconceived representations. The coincidences of becoming human thus lies in the unpredictability of the convergence of causes. When the first ugly mammals originated from earlier reptiles, nobody could have predicted their chances ... ; when the first fishes crawled onto dry land, the question of whether octopus brains were more suitable, was not yet settled."

SCIENTIFIC OBJECTIONS: Palaeontology is primarily concerned with the emplacement of fossil finds in an evolutionary structure. However, no fossils of intermediate forms have ever been found (discussed more fully in [J2]). At present there is a full complement of competing hypotheses, and no unified representation exists [H2]. On informatical/ theoretical grounds it can be stated that there will never be a phylogenetically based genealogical tree of man [G9], because there is no source of new information in evolution. Changing environmental conditions (for example a different climate, or changed biotopes) do not qualify as a source of information for new biological structures.

THE BIBLE: The following aspects in the creation of man are clearly described in the biblical account:

1. *Plan:* It is so trivial that it seems unnecessary even to mention it, but the purpose (intention, concept, plan) of each act of creation is explicitly stated beforehand. In Genesis 1:26 this purposefulness is clearly formulated: "Let us make man." We find the same expression of the will of God in Revelation 4:11: "... by your will they were created and have their being." These testimonies leave no room for a purely coincidental evolutionary origin of man over millions of years.

2. *Implementation:* The best concepts are worthless, unless they have real applicability. But what God decides, He accomplishes: "So God created man in his own image, in the image of God He created him; male and female He created them" (Gen 1:27). This verse concisely describes the "making" of man, which is explained in mo-

re detail in Gen 2:7 (compare Fig 21 in [G5 p 169]). It also provides a glimpse of the conceptual purpose: Man was made in God's likeness, in His image. We are His work; we have been created purposefully!

3. *Conclusion:* By the merging of the "dust of the ground" and "the breath of life" something completely new emerged in creation: "… and man became a living being" (Gen 2:7).

According to the Bible man has been directly created by God. The three phases of creation of man as described in Genesis resemble an engineering project, as is customary in the production of industrial goods. These general principles are as apparent in the manufacture of a simple stapler, as when high performance computers are made. All these artifacts have been preconceived – intellectually planned. It is unrealistic and contrary to all our experiences to ignore preconception in the case of creation. All evolutionary concepts are mired in a materialistic matrix and are therefore methodically insufficient for explaining the origin of man. How can an agnostic "leitmotif" come to grips with a God-given spirit? It is an "a priori" fallacy based on false presuppositions (see assumption E3).

3.2 The Origin of Human Language (OB2)

EVOLUTION: In the evolutionary model human language is regarded as having evolved, although many hypotheses in this respect have been rejected in the light of new knowledge of the phenomenon of speech. According to *Bernhard Rensch* the development of language reflects the uniqueness of man. He concedes [R1 p 141, 142]: "We do not know at what stage of human descent language originated", nevertheless he postulates that "an increase of the number of cells in the frontal lobe of the brain resulted in the development of the motoric speech centre on one side." The existence of today's profusion of languages is also explained in terms of evolution; for example *Illies* states [I2 p 53]: "The existence of many thousands of languages and dialects forces to deduce that ... diversification from common roots had occurred, thus there was an evolution that must have had a point of origin."

SCIENTIFIC OBJECTIONS:

1. The morphological requirements for speech do not rely on the existence of a single organ, but depend on the simultaneous availability of a voice-producing mechanism, a suitable throat cavity (together with the tongue), and a highly complex control system (the brain). How is it possible that such a diverse and exactly matching set of components could have developed together, when – in the words of *Konrad Lorenz* – mutation and selection are the "driving forces" of evolution? It is totally unreasonable to believe that such a marvellous structure could have originated without purpose.

2. When a child is born, it has no command of language, but it is able to learn the language of its parents. The language "supply" is available, and must be "installed" in the baby's brain. But the so-called primitive people, as postulated by evolution, did not have a language source. The situation can be compared to a computer with no software – it can accomplish nothing; no speech could have developed.

3. *H Gipper*, a linguist of Münster (Germany), voiced his misgivings as follows [G1 p 73]:

   "All assumptions that human speech developed gradually from animal grunts (the so-called woof-woof theories) or that gestures changed incrementally into audible language, cannot be sustained. Such erroneous hypotheses compare the specifics of human speech with the communication systems of animals. It can be stated emphatically that the essence of human speech is not communication. Communication exists everywhere in the animal kingdom. But human language is in the first place a knowledge medium; this encompasses an intellectual/spiritual access to the observable world. The essence of speech lies in the possibility of assigning specific meanings to articulated sounds, thereby making them mentally accessible."

4. Language has no selection value. *Gipper* states [G1 p 73]: "In her dissertation on human speech and its biological prerequisites, *Beate Marquardt* assumes that language was not at all necessary for survival in the existence struggle. Speech is regarded as a luxury ... Furthermore, *W von Humboldt* expressed the opinion that human beings did not require speech for mutual help, and referred in this respect to elephants which are extremely social animals without using any form of speech."

5. In various experiments with chimpanzees American researchers (e. g. the *Gardner* couple with Washoe; *Premack* with Sarah) attempted to confirm an evolutionary development of speech. They rendered science a similarly good service as, in an earlier era, those who tried to discover perpetual motion. The impossibility of building a machine that can run without requiring a source of energy, consistently reinforced the law of energy conservation. The ape experiments confirmed that real speech exists nowhere in the animal world; even the most diligent training never resulted in anything possessing the essential characteristics of human speech. Certain concepts could only be developed in cases where the primary survival instincts of the animals were involved.

6. Speech is a non-material phenomenon; that is why all evolutionary hypotheses for its origin fail. This aspect

is discussed more fully in the relevant chapter in [G7 p 115-135].

THE BIBLE: Speech researcher *Gipper* came to the significant conclusion [G1 p 65]: "Anybody who asks questions about the origin of speech, ... has already separated himself from the Bible." Indeed, theories on the origin of speech which have been increasing steadily since the "enlightenment", are all directed against biblical pronouncements. Only the German *Johann Peter Süssmilch* (1707-1767) affirmed: "If it is supposed that man himself was the inventor, then he should already, before the invention of speech, have made use of another kind of language. Man must have been clever and resourceful without possessing speech, and this is evidently impossible. Then only God's intelligence remains."

The Bible affirms that God spoke to Adam, who understood what he was told. This confirms that the first man, Adam, already possessed the God-given gift of speech in all its fullness. He was able to converse intelligently (Gen 2:23, Gen 3:2, 10, 12, 13) and even had the ability to create new words: "So the man gave names to all the livestock, the birds of the air and all the beasts of the field" (Gen 2:20).

Because of man's pride when the tower of Babel was built, God imposed the judgement of the confusion of man's language. When trying to explain the present profusion of languages, one has to consider this event. It is possible to research the splitting off and the development of new languages since then. And it is significant that no increases in complexity have been found. On the contrary, there are very many examples of simplification (e. g. Latin *"insula"* → English *"isle"*; French *"île"*). The previously mentioned assumption by *Illies* of the evolutionary origin of languages from simple roots, is contradicted by reality. The grammar of the classical languages (Greek and Latin) is much more complex than that of present-day languages such as English.

3.3   The Origin of the Sexes (OB3)

EVOLUTION: *B Rensch* regards sexuality as an essential evolutionary factor that is co-responsible for our being here at all [R1 p 64]: "Without sexual differentiation the line of descent would have been much slower and probably would not have reached the present high level, so that man would not have developed." *R W Kaplan* sees a similar meaning for evolution and the sexual differentiation which was spawned by it [K1 p 231]: "The 'invention' of sexual reproduction is certainly the one decisive cause for the development of the higher plants and animals to much more complex levels of organisation."

SCIENTIFIC OBJECTIONS: Through fertilisation new combinations of genes continually arise, so that many variants come into existence, and only those, according to the evolutionary view, who fit the environment best, survive. However, this process is excluded from any upward trend in the line of descent, because no essentially new information arises as a result of the recombinations occurring in sexual reproduction. Through all their countless recombination efforts, all breeders of plants and animals have provided proof that even the most highly bred cows remain cows, and that sunflowers never grow from wheat.

Sexual reproduction is only possible when both sexes have fully functional reproductive organs at the same time. By definition (see assumption E8) an evolutionary process is not directed by some purposeful strategic plan. How is it then possible that such different and complex organs, which fit one another in every morphological and physiological detail, could have evolved suddenly? Furthermore, we must bear in mind – as *Kaplan* concedes – that "the profusion of ways and means is enormous and the sophistication of the tricks the sexes employ to come together, is often astoundingly marvellous; their study is one of the most interesting fields in biology." The question arises why *Rensch* still believes that "no wise Creator was necessary for their origin" [R1 p 66].

THE BIBLE: In the creation account it is repeatedly emphasised that God originally provided the capacity for reproduction. The plants bear "seeds according to their kinds" (Gen 1:12), and the animals were commanded by God to "increase in number" (Gen 1:22). Each kind was equipped and enabled to reproduce itself in its own way. Human beings also did not rely on the supposed "invention" of sexuality for their origin. It was God's idea to create man and woman differently, apart from the animals: "So God created man ... *male and female* He created them" (Gen 1:27). Man was also commanded to "be fruitful and increase in number" (Gen 1:28).

3.4 The Origin of Marriage (OB4)

EVOLUTION: Marriage has not been established by God, neither did it exist from the beginning, rather, it was socially acquired in the framework of cultural evolution. *Robert Havemann* [H3 p 121] describes the evolution of matrimony as follows: "In primitive societies everybody – men and women – were equal. There were no matrimonial unions, but so-called group marriages existed. These groups had no rules about who could have intercourse with whom." Similarly a development from a matriarchy (Latin *"mater"* = mother; women ruling) to a patriarchy (Latin *"pater"* = father; men ruling) is assumed.

THE BIBLE: Marriage is a gift of God. When God brought to Adam the woman who was specially created for him, he cried out joyfully: "This is now bone of my bones and flesh of my flesh" (Gen 2:23). This joy over a real companion is the explicit will of God: "It is not good for the man to be alone. I will make a helper suitable for him" (Gen 2:18). Marriage has been established by the Creator; it is therefore not a humanly devised institution. It existed from the beginning, as Jesus Himself defined the origin and essence of marriage in Matthew 19:4-6: "Haven't you read ... that at the beginning the Creator 'made them male and female', and said (Gen 2:24), 'for this reason a man will leave his father and mother and be united to his wife, and the two will become one flesh'? So they are no longer two, but one. Therefore what God has joined together, let man not separate." With the commandment "You shall not commit adultery", God protects marriage and allows sexual intercourse only inside this close union (Eccl 9:9). Sexual relations (becoming one flesh) before or outside marriage is branded as fornication and immorality.

The supposed evolutionary development from a matriarchy to a patriarchy is biblically false. The woman was originally given as a "helper" (Gen 2:18), but not as a ruler of the man. Through Paul Christ also confirmed this revelation in the New Testament: "Now I want you to realise that the head of every man is Christ, and the head of the woman is man, and the head of Christ is God" (1 Cor 11:3). The role assigned to men neither leads to a slavish submission of women as in Islam, nor to the rivalry aspired to by women's lib. The God-given relationship between man and woman is expressed most clearly in the comparison with the relationship between Christ and the church: "Now as the church submits to Christ, so also wives should submit to their husbands in everything. Husbands, love your wives, just as Christ loved the church and gave himself up for her ..." (Eph 5:24-25).

3.5 The Origin of Death (OB5)

The evolutionary view of death underscores and reveals the impossibility of reconciling evolution with Biblical doctrine. This question will therefore be discussed in detail.

EVOLUTION: The following four basic tenets, substantiated by many references, can be deduced:

1. *Death is an essential prerequisite for evolution:* In evolutionary thought death plays a fundamental role; it is a necessary precondition for the succession of postulated events. *C F von Weizsäcker* states [W3]: "If individuals did not die, evolution would not have been possible, and no new organisms with new characteristics could have originated. Evolution requires the death of individuals." *Hans Mohr*, a biologist from Freiburg, made a similar statement [M2 p 12]: "No life could have existed if there were no death. Death as such was not caused by evolution. Rather, the death of individuals is required to ensure the development of the tribe. There is no way past this precept, this axiom of the doctrine of evolution. Without the death of individuals there could have been no evolution of life on this earth. If we regard the evolution of life as a positive result, as 'the real creation', then we accept our own death as a positive creative factor." The strong contrast with the Bible, which explicitly characterises death as a hostile power, now becomes clear (1 Cor 15:26, Rev 6:8).

2. *Death is an invention of evolution:* Prof *Widmar Tanner* of Regensburg (Germany), who, as a biologist, concerned himself with the question of death, concluded that the known laws of physics and chemistry which also hold for biology, at no point force us to assume that a biological system must grow old and die. From this viewpoint he asks: "How and why did death enter our

world when it should not properly be here?" He assumes that evolution itself invented death as a significant factor [T1 p 46]: "Aging and length of life are adaptive phenomena which developed in certain specific ways for each kind during the course of evolution ... The process of evolution was speeded up substantially by the invention of death." He regards the introduction of death as an opportunity for chance to try out new developments.

For *Ludwig von Bertalanffy* death is the calculated price that had to be paid for upward development, that "dynamic drama full of tension and tragic complications" [B3]: "With great effort life rose up to increasingly sophisticated levels, paying for each advance. Unicellular organisms developed into multi-cellular beings, thereby introducing death." That which the Bible describes as a judgment on sin, is heralded by evolutionists as a necessary product of evolution [R2 p 290]: "Death entered this world when multi-cellular organisms developed; pain was introduced when the nervous system originated, and fear was the result of consciousness ... possessions resulted in worry, and the development of morality caused doubts and uncertainty."

3. *Death is the creator of life:* The anti-biblical character of evolution becomes quite clear when its advocates elevate death to be the creator of life. Microbiologist *R W Kaplan* explains this as follows [K1 p 236]:

"For bisexual organisms this preprogrammed death has an additional function: The limited life expectancy and the limitations of sexuality prevent the interchange of genes between successive generations, that is, between 'obsolete' predecessors and 'progressive' descendants. Aging and death prevent backward fertilisation and thus promote evolution. For the individual aging and death is unavoidable and distressing, especially in the case of human beings, but it is the price that had to be paid for our existence, through evolution."

Tanner also emphasises the creative role of death [T1 p 51]: "It is not a very comforting thought that man would probably not have developed if there were no death. But when it comes to aging and death, one should not expect any consolation from a biologist." *Hans Mohr* answers his own question about the developmental programme that invariably leads to death, as follows [M1 p 12]: "Because our kind, because homo sapiens came into being as a result of evolution. The temporal limits of individual life is the unavoidable prerequisite for the emergence of man."

4. *Death, the final and absolute termination of life:* According to evolutionary doctrines life is a condition of matter based solely on physical and chemical laws *(M Eigen)*. This reduction of reality to exclusively material phenomena leaves no room for life after death. Man is reduced to a biological machine, and his death is on a par with that of any organism. In the cogs and mechanisms of evolution the purpose of death is to give rise to new life. A person's life is regarded as a mere contribution to the progress of evolution [K1 p 236]. Even when death researcher *Elisabeth Kübler-Ross* refers to life after death, she only considers its contribution to evolution [K2 p 185]: "The obligation of personal maturity requires that every single person contributes to the maturity and evolutionary development of the entire species. In this way everyone fulfils his or her destiny. Death is the key to evolution." Let us not be misled: What appears to be Christian terminology, proves to be false on closer inspection.

SCIENTIFIC OBJECTIONS: Science can tell us nothing about the origin and essence of death, because it lies beyond the reach of scientific methods. Consequently medical science is only concerned with the precise moment of death (brain death or the cessation of cardiac activity).

THE BIBLE: The Bible explicitly states that the earth and all life came into being by direct creative acts of God. When creation was finished, God pronounced it completed and described it as "very good". God is Love. He is full of mercy, and He created everything through Jesus (John 1:10, Col 1:16) and through His wisdom (Col 2:3). In creation He was true to Himself, because He does not change (James 1:17, Hebr 13:8). That is completely different from the evolutionary "strategy" of pain and tears, gruesomeness and death. Anybody who regards God as the cause of evolution by assuming such a method of creation, distorts God's nature into something contrary to itself. Then what is the origin of death if it is neither an evolutionary factor nor derives from God?

We know that death is everywhere. All people die, including recently born babies as well as the aged, people with high moral standards and also thieves and robbers; believers and unbelievers, all are subject to death. Such a universal and radical effect must have a universal cause. The Bible states that death is a result of human sin. Although God had warned the man and woman (Gen 2:17), they misused the freedom given them and thus fell into sin. From that moment the law of sin came into effect: "The wages of sin is death" (Rom 6:23). Man found himself on the thick black line of death as indicated in Figure 1. Since the time of Adam who was responsible for the introduction of death (1 Tim 2:14), all of mankind is bound by this chain of death: "Therefore, just as sin entered the world through one man, and death through sin, and in this way death came to all men, because all sinned" (Rom 5:12). Before the fall into sin death was unknown throughout creation. Although the Bible unambiguously emphasises this fact, the doctrine of a perfect, untainted original creation has been widely forsaken and sold out in present-day university theology. They have been misguided by philosophers like *Lessing, Kant* and *Hegel*, who described man's fall into sin as the starting point of man's history of freedom and progress. But according to the Bible man was originally good, with no pain, sickness or death. Even in the apocryphical book, the Wisdom of Solomon (1:13), it is explicitly stated that death was not a component of the original creation: "But God did not make death, nor is He pleased with the destruction of the living."

When the Bible refers to death, it is never in the sense of a termination of existence. The biblical definition of death means "to be separated from ..." Because man's sin encompass a threefold death (Figure 1), it implies three kinds of separation:

1. **Spiritual death:** At the moment of the first sin man "died spiritually", meaning that he was separated from communion with God. Today everybody who does not believe in the Creator, finds him- or herself in this condition. They have no relationship with Jesus Christ, nor with the message of the Bible; they are spiritually dead, although they may be physically very much alive.

2. **Physical death:** A second result was the death of the body: "... until you return to the ground, since from it you were taken" (Gen 3:19).

3. **Eternal death:** The line of death finally leads to eternal death; but man's existence is not terminated (Luke 16:19-31). It is the final situation of being separated from God. God's wrath rests on him, because "the result of one trespass was condemnation for all men" (Rom 5:18).

The bridge between God and man collapsed when man sinned. Anybody who moves along in life without considering this breach, will end up in the abyss because of the threefold death. Is there an alternative? God is not only wrathful towards sin, but He is a God of love who loves the sinner. Anybody can leave the train which is speeding towards the destination "eternal death" because of man's sin, and cross over to the train of life moving towards the destination called "eternal life". Eternal life or eternal death is the final destination of our imperishable existence; we have been created for eternity. Which way we go, is our choice as free creatures: "I have set before you (eternal) life and (eternal) death, blessing and curses. Now choose life" (Deut 30:19). It is abundantly clear that God's will and purpose for us is life.

The following simple but extremely important corollary can be derived from Figure 1:

> "If you have only been born once (physical birth), then you die twice (the body dies first, followed by eternal death);
>
> but if you have been born twice (physical birth and born-again spiritually), then you only die once (physical death)!"

The biblical doctrine of redemption is very closely linked to the doctrine of death (Rom 5:12, 14; Rom 6:23; 1 Cor 15:21). Belief in the Son of God frees us from the damnatory judgment and assures us of eternal life: "Whoever hears my word and believes him who sent me, has eternal life and will not be condemned; he has crossed over from (spiritual) death to (eternal) life (John 5:24).

When considering the implications of this decision, the tragic effect that evolution and its view of death has on evolutionists, becomes quite clear. The danger of eternal death is eclipsed, and many people miss the offer of salvation. Adherents of theistic evolution accept the evolutionary view of death. Then one assumes that God employed this hostile power (1 Cor 15:26) to create living beings. But the New Testament earnestly warns: "Do not let anyone … disqualify you for the prize" (Col 2:18).

Figure 1:

Since man's fall into sin, all people by their very nature (Rom 5:14) find themselves on the broad road leading to damnation according to the Bible (Mat 7:13b). The final destination of this train of death which travels via the stations of spiritual and physical death, is eternal death. However, it is the expressed will of God (e. g. 1 Tim 2:4; 2 Peter 3:9b) that man should make, by his own free will, the decision (Deut 30:19; Jer 21:8; 1 Tim 6:12) to leave the train of death, pass through the narrow gate (Matt 7:13a, 14) and enter the train of life which will take him to everlasting life. Jesus described this change of trains as the only and all-important breakthrough to eternal life (John 5:24). To human beings equipped with a free will this opportunity presents itself only in their lifespan on earth. This "new birth" (John 3:3) is based on Jesus' death on the cross (John 3:16; Rom 5:10) and is directly available for everybody who personally accepts the "message of the cross" (1 Cor 1:18).

(Questions asked frequently in this context are: What happens to those people who have never heard the gospel? How about those who lived before Jesus came? How about the under-aged (e. g. babies) who have not been able to personally take a decision? In [G4] the author tries to give an answer to these questions that is based on the Bible.)

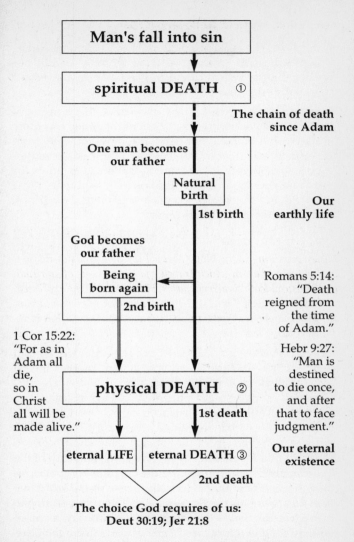

Figure 1: *The narrow way and the broad road (Matthew 7:13-14)*

43

3.6 The Origin of Religions (OB6)

EVOLUTION: The existence of all religions is understood as a developmental process, starting from a simple polytheism, monotheism (Judaism, Christianity and Islam) eventually emerged.

SCIENTIFIC OBJECTIONS: On the one hand, the transfer of evolutionary concepts to the origin of religions, was quite arbitrary, but on the other hand, it follows logically from the principles of evolution (compare the basic evolutionary assumption E2). There are no historical grounds for this presupposition. The application of evolutionary ideas to the Bible is in complete contrast with biblical doctrines, and has rather grave implications:

1. No distinction is made between divine revelation and conceptual structures contrived by men (Gal 1:12 ; Rev 1:1).

2. Biblical pronouncements are reduced to the level of human endeavour.

3. The difference between salvation and damnation is ignored.

Lutz von Padberg maintains [P1 p 44]: "From the biblical perspective it is a false doctrine to assign 'another special way of salvation' to other religions, because they are anti-Christian by nature and purpose ... Man's resistance to the biblical affirmation that he is human and therefore cannot be a godlike superman (compare Genesis 3:22), leads to a perversion of the biblical distinction between God and man. Man will not acknowledge the truth of the Creator, and thus simply turns the creation account upside down, perverting it in the true sense of the word: He does not want to be God's image, but turns God into man's image. That is the origin of religions which consequently contain many gap fillers borrowed from the Christian faith, exactly because they are based on 'what may be known about God' as mentioned by Paul in Romans 1:19."

THE BIBLE: All people have three fundamental types of information at their disposal, given them at creation according to the Bible:

1. The wonders seen in creation lead to the conclusion that a Creator must have been at work (Romans 1:19-21; for a teleological view, see basic assumption C8).

2. Our conscience bears witness that we are guilty before God (Rom 2:14-15).

3. We all possess some inkling of Eternity, because God has implanted it in our hearts (Eccl 3:11).

Man's inventiveness was extraordinarily moved by this universal knowledge, leading to thousands of peculiar ways in the form of various religions. The distinction between man's religious way and God's way already became clear with Cain and Abel. Cain was the first person who wanted to serve God according to his own ideas; he thus became the founder of the first religion. Cain did not at all practise polytheism as envisioned by evolutionists for the first religion. His brother acted according to God's will and is held up as an example of having a faith that pleases God (Hebr 11:4). Our chain of faith reaches back through Abraham, Noah and Enoch, and all the way back to the first man. This illustrates the fact that God-pleasing faith was present right from the very beginning (monotheism therefore did not evolve), and other religions arose concurrently, being mere human constructs. Although Cain addressed the God of the Bible by his offering, it was frowned upon and not accepted in grace (Gen 4:5). It thus becomes very clear that all religions which do not pay homage to the Father of Jesus Christ, are denounced by God as idolatry and witchcraft (Lev 26:1, Ps 31:7; Jer 10:14-15; 2 Cor 6:16). From time to time the idea that adherents of other religions are also finding their way to God, is advocated, but it is unambiguously and emphatically rejected by the Bible: "For all the gods of the nations are idols" (Ps 96:5), and "No ... idolater – has any inheritance in the kingdom of Christ and of God" (Eph 5:5). The decisive distinction between the origin of biblical faith (God-given) and the religions (contrived by man) has crucial consequences: While God's way brings eternal salvation, the religions obstruct the way to redemption (see [G4] for a more detailed discussion).

3.7 The so-called "Fundamental Law of Biogenetics" (OB7)

EVOLUTION: Of all *Darwin's* (1809-1882) contemporaries *Ernst Haeckel* (1834-1919) was the most vehement German adherent of evolution. He formulated the "fundamental law of biogenetics" which states that animals and man reflect all stages of their evolutionary descent during their embryonic development. He and his successors proclaimed this "law" as one of the strongest arguments in support of evolution. This line of reasoning still crops up in present-day school textbooks.

SCIENTIFIC OBJECTIONS: Even the convinced evolutionist *Bernhard Rensch* accedes [R1 p 89-90]: "The 'basic biogenetic law' formulated by Haeckel, states that the development of individuals provides a brief recapitulation of their descent. This view is not valid, because one cannot equate embryonic stages with the adult stages of their predecessors." *D S Peters* of the *Senckenberg Institute* (Frankfurt/Main; Germany) makes it even clearer [P3 p 67]: "The basic biogenetic law as well as all similar statements lead to only one conclusion: Forget it. This sounds radical, but it is the only measure that will prevent phylogenetics to be practised in the future with false and irrelevant arguments." He pleads that "we should now lay the fundamental law of biogenetics to rest in the archives of history." *Erich Blechschmidt* of Göttingen, a well-known authority on human embryology, based his "law of the conservation of individuality" on decades of research. This law is just as important for biology as the law of the conservation of energy is for physics [B4]. He exposed *Haeckel's* basic law as one of the most profound fallacies. The so-called gill slits appearing early in the development of the human foetus was seen as providing historical proof of the development of man; as a kind of recapitulation. *Blechschmidt's* research enabled him to refute this assumption, because the "gill slits" are simply folds lying between the forehead and the heart clump at one stage of this purposeful and dynamic growth process. See [J3] for further particulars.

THE BIBLE: Some people are of the opinion that, after God had created everything, He did not interfere with the operation of this "wound-up clock". This idea (deism) which originated in England in the time of the "enlightenment", is definitely not found in the Bible. God is the ever active Lord who rules history, as is emphatically clear from the example of the Israelites. In particular He intervened when His Son Jesus Christ was sent to the world. And even the embryonic development of every single person implies a direct act of the Creator: "For You created my inmost being; You knit me together in my mother's womb. I praise You because I am fearfully and wonderfully made; Your works are wonderful, I know that full well" (Ps 139:13-14). When Jeremiah was called, God told him that this assignment had been planned for him before his conception: "Before I formed you in the womb I knew you, before you were born, I set you apart; I appointed you as a prophet to the nations" (Jer 1:5). The Psalmist also knew of these creative acts of God performed long before his birth (Ps 139:16).

If our present-day laws were based on the Bible and not on evolutionistic views, abortion would not have become common-place. In Germany mothers' bodies have become the prime site for committing murder, since the number of lives snuffed out in one year is equal to the entire population of the German town Braunschweig. There is one abortion for every three births. This is happening in one of the richest countries of the world and it is motivated by "social convenience". The sin of lying is added to the sin of murder.

3.8 The Essential Nature of Man (OB8)

EVOLUTION: In the evolutionary system the body/soul/ spirit reality of man is the victim of an improper reductionism. According to this view matter and mind are essentially indistinguishable; they only differ in their degree of complexity. As *Wuketits* writes [W5 p 140]: "Although physical structures and the corresponding psychological phenomena are two spheres which have been interlinked by evolution, they comprise different levels of complexity … We may thus speak of a natural spiritual condition in the literary sense of the word, and so express the hope that the old body/soul dichotomy has finally been abolished." The co-founder of Marxism, *Friedrich Engels*, had previously aired similar views: "The material world to which we belong and which can be observed by our senses, is the only reality … Matter is not a mental precept, on the contrary, mind is merely the highest product of matter." Mental evolution is regarded as a third type, after chemical and organic evolution, by *Hellmuth Benesch*, who is an evolutionist psychologist [B2 p 19]: "The mind also evolved. We can, so to speak, refer to a palaeontology of the soul."

SCIENTIFIC OBJECTIONS: The behavioural psychologist *Hans Zeier* affirms that we cannot really formulate direct conclusions about the origin and true nature of the human mind (spirit) from a scientific viewpoint [E1 p 15]. Whenever mind and its origin is mentioned in evolutionary statements, these are never based on scientific results, but always on evolutionistic presuppositions. For example, *H Benesch* [B2 p 147] writes: "One of the most crucial and consistent tenets of this book is to regard psychological aspects not only as having an evolutionary origin, but to establish and respect this origin." This once again reveals the evolutionary assumption E1: Evolution is not the result of scientific research; rather, facts that support the presupposed doctrine, are being sought. *Benesch* still has to demonstrate that "psychic processes gradually developed from the functions of the nervous system." And he warns [B2 p 147]: "As we may deduce from the history of biological descent, it was no easy scientific saunter. The road ahead is just as hard and rocky." He also sees himself on a road going in a direction parallel to *Darwin* [B2 p 14]: "Notwithstanding the limitedness of *Darwin's* knowledge, his teachings on origins and descent achieved remarkable success. One can thus appreciate the negligence of the psychologists. Very many of them are still reluctant to construct a psychology based on evolution … There is an opportunity for a great leap forward in the psycho-cybernetic aspects of the problem of the origin of man's mind (spirit)."

Those schools of psychology (*Watson's* and *Skinner's* behaviourism, *K Lorenz's* instinctivism) based on a one-dimensional, materialistic view of man – which are therefore evolutionistic – can today be regarded as totally obsolete, because they excluded important aspects like freedom, responsibility, and destructivity. *Sigmund Freud* recognised a transcendental portion of the mind, an independent structure having its own laws and rules, and he was the first to rise above a narrow determinism. *Erich Fromm* developed this model further, allocating essential roles to personal identity and free will. Freedom, responsibility, and voluntary choices between good and bad, all play an appropriate role.

One should also note the dualistic interaction theory of *John Eccles*, a Nobel prize winner, who justifiably bewails the current unrealistic materialistic theories [E1]. He consequently concludes that death is not the end of human existence [E1 p 190]: "The components of our existence in the second world are not of a material nature, and are therefore not necessarily subject to the dissolution that befalls all components of the individual which belong to the first world."

In the evolutionary view one encounters an unbridgeable chasm between matter and mind, brain and consciousness, and body and soul, since only material components are considered according to basic assumption E3. *Horst W Beck* mentions the problem of scientifically describing the entire person: "When regarded reflectively, one's immediate reality can only be circumstantial. Man is and remains his own greatest puzzle." It is scientifically untenable to regard man only from a materialistic viewpoint, as is done by evolutionists.

THE BIBLE: It is impossible to understand human nature apart from biblical revelation. In our context it is unimportant whether we consider man to be a threefold being (the trichotomy body/soul/spirit as seen by *H W Beck* and *W Nee*), or as having only two components (dichotomy of body/soul(mind) according to *J Neidhart*). As already stated in OB1, one must, in the case of human beings, clearly distinguish between material (body: Greek *"soma"*) and immaterial components (soul: Hebrew *"nephesh"*, 754 times in the Old Testament, Greek *"psyche"*, 101 times in the NT; spirit: Hebrew *"ruach"*, 378 times in the OT, Greek *"pneuma"*, 379 times in the NT). In 1 Thessalonians 5:23 we find a basic statement concerning a structural description of man: "May God himself, the God of peace, sanctify you through and through. May your whole spirit, soul and body be kept blameless at the coming of our Lord Jesus Christ." By definition, all evolutionary concepts allow material considerations only, and all of them are revealed to be limited by this pronouncement. Spirit and soul are immaterial constituents, and the Bible gives explicitly clear descriptions of their origin (Gen 2:7) and their destination after death (Eccl 12:14; Ps 16:10). When Adam sinned, man's spirit became sick unto death. But when a person repents (see Figure 1), he is born again, his spirit comes alive. This event is essential in our earthly life for salvation.

3.9   Human Behaviour (OB9)

The question of whether man is inherently "good" or "evil", has inspired many poets and philosophers to produce a plethora of theatre plays, poems, and tales. All philosophies are based on the assumption that man is inherently good (e. g. humanism, Marxism). Let us now consider the evolutionistic view.

EVOLUTION: Many statements confirm the unanimous opinion that man is aggressive and selfish. *Joachim Illies* [I1 p 85], a biologist, writes: "The human fist, as a means of showing and implementing aggression, is in fact a tangible proof for the development of man." A biologist from Freiburg, *Hans Mohr* [M2 p 16-17], emphasises this further: "The origin of man, as homo sapiens, occurred towards the end of the Pleistocene – as a result of natural selection in a battle with other hominids and other men. An irrefutable conclusion is that hate and aggression and the tendency to kill are inherent … murder, homicide, torture, and genocide characterise the cultural history of man. The murdering children of *Pol Pots* are no singular excess, but the rule. It should be obvious that even the ritualisation of murder to the point of being acceptably cultivated, as in knightly battles and duels and in Haager's war ordinances, has the same genetic origin as blind, merciless, lustful murder." *Mohr* is compelled to ask: "How did we acquire these appalling genes?" His answer that the eggshells of evolution still cling to us, fits well in the evolutionary scheme of things, but it is biblically false, as we shall see now.

THE BIBLE: Human nature is by no means described by the Bible as good. A clear picture of God's diagnosis of man's condition emerges from only a few passages:

Genesis 8:21: "… every inclination of his heart is evil from childhood."

Psalm 14:3:
"They have all turned aside, they have together become corrupt; there is no-one who does good, not even one."

Isaiah 1:5-6:
"Your whole head is injured, your whole heart is afflicted. From the sole of your foot to the top of your head there is no soundness …"

Matthew 15:19:
"For out of the heart come evil thoughts, murder, adultery, sexual immorality, theft, false testimony, slander."

The factual conclusions about human nature in the Bible and in evolutionistic thought are similar. But the causes of this reality lie worlds apart. What evolution describes as an inevitable heritage from the animal kingdom, the Bible regards as a consequence of sin. This crucial event marks the change from "image of God" (Gen 1:27) to an evil (Gen 8:21), mortal (Ps 90:5-9) and lost being (2 Cor 4:3). Man was not created evil, but only became evil after he had sinned. Two fundamentally different and divergent paths follow: If man is sinful, then he requires salvation (see paragraph 8.5); if his evil state is a result of his evolutionary origin, then salvation is of no concern.

4. Astronomical Observations

4.1 The Origin of the Universe (OB10)

The British professor of theoretical physics, *Paul Davies*, clearly outlined the problematical questions concerning the origin of the universe [D1 p 10]:

> "If the universe had no origin in time – if it has always existed – then it is of infinite age. The concept of infinity leaves many people reeling. If there has been an infinite number of events already, why do we find ourselves living now? Did the universe remain quiescent for all of eternity only to spring into action relatively recently, or has there been some activity going on for ever and ever? On the other hand, if the universe *began*, that means accepting it appeared suddenly out of nothing. This seems to imply that there was a first event. If so, what caused it?"

EVOLUTION: According to the standard cosmological model the universe originated in the so-called "big bang". It follows from present observations that the *Hubble* constant, $H = 55$ (km/s)/Mpc $= 1.78 \cdot 10^{-18}$ s^{-1}, represents the initial rate of expansion of the universe. On assuming a constant rate of expansion, the inverse value $1/H = 18 \cdot 10^9$ years gives the moment in time when all matter was supposedly compressed in one point. The age of the universe is defined by means of this extreme extrapolation. The chronology of evolutionary cosmology is based on Table 1, according to *R Breuer* [B8 p 86]. (see next page)

In this scheme the earth is very much a latecomer in our universe. Allegedly it split off from the sun or from the mass surrounding the sun. Astronomer *O Heckmann* cau-

Time since big bang	the Event
0	Big bang
1 week	Radiation becomes thermic
10 000 years	Condensation of matter
1000 to 2000 million yrs	Formation of galaxies
3000 million yrs	Formation of galaxy clusters
4100 million yrs	Formation of stars
15 200 mill. yrs	Primeval sun nebula
15 400 mill. yrs	Formation of the planets (incl. the earth)
16 100 mill. yrs	Formation of the oldest earth rocks
18 000 mill. yrs	Development of an oxygen-rich atmosphere

Table 1: Chronology of evolutionary cosmology
(according to *R Breuer*)

tions [H4 p 132]: "The conclusions could eventually become so inaccurate that the connection with the empirical origin of the chain may be practically lost. This is common to all scientific deductions, and holds in particular in cosmology where infinite extrapolations abound."

SCIENTIFIC OBJECTIONS: The assumption that the rate of expansion has ALWAYS been the same (see basic evolutionary assumption E10), is purely arbitrary. Furthermore, it is assumed that the calculated time spans really occurred. What will happen if such a long time span before the present was not available? The question of the origin of matter has in any case not been answered. In his book "Die ersten drei Minuten" (The first three minutes) [W2 p 119] *Steven Weinberg* concedes that the big bang theory is pure speculation:

> "In following this account of the first three minutes, the reader may feel that he can detect a note of scientific overconfidence. He might be right ... It is often necessary to forget one's doubts and to follow the consequences of one's assumptions wherever they may lead ... This does not mean that it is

54

true ... Nevertheless, there *is* one great uncertainty that hangs like a dark cloud over the standard model (= the big bang)."

The declared purpose of cosmology is to understand the structure, operation, and origin of the universe and the earth only "in the framework of natural laws". This restriction precludes the planning and purposeful acts of a Creator God; furthermore, we find ourselves outside the scope of science (see basic assumption C6). The purely materialistic constraint posed by *Wuketits* [W5 p 98], has no scientific basis: "No 'a priori' purpose exists ... There is no planning Spirit, since evolution itself is the planner and creates its own laws." Many scientific objections can be raised against the above model; we mention only two:

1. 98 per cent of the rotational energy of the solar system is found in the planets, although they only comprise 1 per cent of the total mass. This exceptional ratio excludes the possibility that the earth and the other planets could have been formed from the mass of the sun.

2. The earth possesses a large number of astronomical and physical peculiarities which make life on earth possible. In addition, the exact values of very many properties must fall inside very restricted bounds, all at the same time. The following prerequisites are exceedingly improbable in the light of the nebular hypothesis (discussed more fully in [G8]):

   – the correct distance between earth and sun

   – the elliptical orbit of the earth around the sun with its small eccentricity

   – the constant energy output of the sun

   – the correct rate of rotation of the earth

   – the optimum tilt angle between the axis of the earth and the ecliptic

- the correct size and mass of the earth
- the correct quantity of carbon dioxide in the atmosphere of the earth
- the correct quantity of oxygen in the atmosphere of the earth
- the correct distance of the moon from the earth.

THE BIBLE: The Bible describes the universe (cosmos) in various terms. In the New Testament the Greek word *"kosmos"* mostly refers to the earth itself (e.g. John 3:16; Hebr 10:5), but often the entire universe is also meant (e.g. Matt 24:31; Acts 17:24). The term *"ta panta"* also encompasses the entire universe (Eph 1:23). The first use of a specific word for the universe in the Old Testament (Hebrew *"hakkol"*) is in Jeremia 10:16: "... for He is the Maker of all things". In the creation account the terms "heaven (Hebr *"shamayim"*) and earth" (Gen 1:1) or *"earth and heaven"* (Gen 2:1) are synonyms for the entire universe. Not only the first verse of the Bible, but many other passages (e.g. Neh 9:6; Ps 102:5) describe God as the Creator of a completed universe, in which the stars did not develop in a process lasting for thousands of millions of years, but they were complete right from the beginning (Hebr 4:3). This is an incontrovertible answer to *Davies'* question about the origin.

The physical law of the conservation of energy states that in our universe energy cannot be created out of nothing, neither can it be destroyed. Now what was the origin of the energy in the universe? The only possibility is an act of creation.

The earth and all the stars in the universe did not originate in a big bang; they were created independently and on different days. On the first day God created the universe containing no stars, but only the earth. Only on the fourth day – when plants already existed – the stars and other planets were created. Thus all stars are of the same age, excluding the three creation days. This differs conceptually and fundamentally completely from the evolutionary model. The earth did not start its career as a glowing ball of fire, but it originally had water on its surface (Gen 1:2). It is not the accidental byproduct of a cosmic explosion, but – as is the case for the entire universe – it was made for a purpose: "In the beginning you laid the foundations of the earth, and the heavens are the work of your hands" (Ps 102:25). During a conversation with Job God clearly explained to him the conceptual (the foundation of all astronomical and physical data) and the geometrical dimensions of the establishment of the earth: "Where were you when I laid the earth's foundation? Tell me, if you understand. Who marked off its dimensions? (or: drew up its constructional plans) Surely you know! Who stretched a measuring line across it?" (Job 38:4). In the light of the biblical revelations the evolutionary view of the origin of the earth and the universe is proved to be a series of false statements.

4.2 The Future of the Universe (OB11)

EVOLUTION: Evolution sees no temporal end to the universe. An astrophysicist like *R Breuer* writes for example [B8 p 49]: "Gravity is the driving force that keeps even an eternally expanding universe in motion against a purely thermic heat death." *Breuer* even lists some speculations about future events. After 10^{20} years the classical evolution of the cosmos will end; it will be followed by a quantum mechanical era and all protons will undergo gravitational collapse after 10^{45} years. "After 10^{1500} years there will be spheres of pure iron in utter darkness at exceedingly low temperatures" (p 55). But even this is not seen as the end. *Freeman Dyson*, a physicist of Princeton, USA, extrapolates across all temporal boundaries: As far into the future as we can imagine, there will always be objects. In an open cosmos history has no end.

SCIENTIFIC OBJECTIONS: We do not know whether we live in an open universe or a closed one; furthermore, the geo-metrical/astronomical structure of the universe is totally unknown. The only honest answer about the future of the universe is that no scientifically based projections can be made.

THE BIBLE: If there is Somebody Who created the world, only He can tell us what really will happen. The Word of God does not describe this world as being in a state of continual development (evolving towards point omega according to *Teilhard de Chardin*), but as being subjected to decay since man's fall into sin (Rom 8:20-21). The Lord Jesus exclaims in Matthew 24:35: "Heaven and earth will pass away ..." This temporal end of the universe is also described in other passages of the Bible:

Psalm 102:25-26:
"In the beginning you laid the foundations of the earth, and the heavens are the work of your hands. They will perish, but you remain; ..."

Isaiah 34:4:
"All the stars of the heavens will be dissolved and the sky rolled up like a scroll; ..."

Isaiah 51:6:
"... the heavens will vanish like smoke, the earth will wear out like a garment ..."

2 Peter 3:10, 13:
"But the day of the Lord will come like a thief. The heavens will disappear with a roar; the elements will be destroyed by fire, and the earth and everything in it will be laid bare ... But in keeping with His promise we are looking forward to a new heaven and a new earth ..."

Revelation 6:14:
"The sky receded like a scroll, rolling up, ..."

4.3 The Centre of the Universe (OB12)

EVOLUTION: When one considers the consequences of the big bang hypothesis, like *Wuketits*, then man is reduced to absolute insignificance on this grain of dust, the earth [W6 p 40]: "The universe is as deaf to our joyful dancing as to our lamentations, and nobody 'out there' in the immeasurable expanses of the cosmos will bemoan the end of a species which has embarked on a course of self-destruction. It pains me to expose this view which resulted from a study of the evolution of man's mind." If one only considers the geometrical position of the earth in our galaxy, then we may appear to be "cosmic outcasts" according to *Nietzsche*, or seem to be *Monod's* "gypsies at the edge of the universe".

SCIENTIFIC VIEW: Present astronomical knowledge recognises no singular geometrical point in our universe – in accordance with evolutionary ideas. Consequently there is no geometrical centre and also no defined edge. No place in the universe has a special position. This means that even *Monod's* statement about an edge is invalid.

THE BIBLE: However, the earth occupies the central position in the entire universe because of its God-given role, even though it may not be in the geometrical centre. The first astronomical object that God created, was the earth; this clearly indicates its importance amongst all of the other stars and planets. The creation account gives a day by day report on the preparation of the earth as man's dwelling place. God's attention focuses on this planet: "To the Lord your God belong the heavens, even the highest heavens, the earth and everything in it" (Deut 10:14). On this planet He implemented most of His creative ideas, as the psalmist cries out: "… the earth is full of your creatures" (Ps 104:24). No other astronomical body is called God's footstool (Isaiah 66:1; Acts 7:49). The clearest indication of the earth's central position is that God's own Son was sent here. Jesus Christ became a human being for our sake. He destroyed man's sin exactly in *that* place where it had been introduced into the universe, namely the earth! The cross of salvation stood on Calvary and no other place in the cosmos. Jesus ascended to heaven from the earth, and He will return here as exalted Lord when He comes again.

These few cosmological considerations from the Bible clearly indicate that evolutionist ideas are completely foreign to Scripture.

5. Biological Observations

5.1 The First Life on Earth (OB13)

EVOLUTION: According to this scheme life could only have originated in water (primeval soup); furthermore, a certain depth of water was required to absorb the lethal ultra-violet rays. After multicellular organisms had developed, an incomprehensible jump by life forms from water to dry land occurred at some unknown moment.

SCIENTIFIC OBJECTIONS: This supposed transition from an aquatic way of life to life on land entails a number of problems that must be resolved in one single animal – and not during successive generations – to enable it to continue living under the new conditions. Some of these problems are discussed now:

1. *Larger body weight:* "the solid will, when weighed in the fluid, be lighter than its weight in air by the weight of the fluid displaced" (*Archimedes'* law). When an organism "decides" to go on land, it must carry its own full weight. This requires solid muscles and a stronger skeleton. The increase in weight also requires 40 % more energy.

2. *New way of breathing:* The oxygen required for metabolic processes must now be obtained from the air instead of from the water. An entirely new oxygenation concept is necessary to prevent a sudden demise.

3. *More difficult disposal of body wastes:* Disposal of metabolic products becomes appreciably more troublesome, because it can no more simply be "sweated out" and washed away by the water. Water must be used sparingly on land. This becomes clear when it is noted

that our kidneys for example can filter waste products out of 150 liters of fluids and discharge only 1 liter of urine.

4. *The problem of evaporation:* Water is a major component of all living organisms. The process of evaporation begins with the supposed transition from water to land. A suitable skin that prevents dehydration, becomes necessary.

5. *Large temperature fluctuations:* During the course of 24 hours the underwater temperature fluctuates very little. On land there can be extreme differences between midday heat and the cold of night. An animal living on land requires suitable measures to cope with such variations.

Consequently, *K Hansen* states the following requirements [H1 p 29]: "The organisms must therefore reach a higher developmental level in the water before they could venture on to dry land." This is an impossibility for evolution. How could any organism have so many fundamental changes at its disposal to be able to survive the transition from water to dry land? *G Osche*, an evolutionary biologist, acknowledges this problem when he concedes [O1 p 58]: "During certain evolutionary phases living organisms cannot simply 'suspend operations due to alterations'."

THE BIBLE: According to the biblical creation account the first life did not originate in water and also did not evolve; the first life forms were created on land. On the third day God created the plants (Gen 1:11-12) as multicellular organisms. Two basic evolutionary assumptions, namely that life originated in water and that the first organism was one single living cell, are biblically false. Aquatic animals were only created on the fifth day (Gen 1:20-23).

5.2 "Each According to its Kind" (OB14)

For biologists kinds of organisms are the fundamental building blocks, just as the chemical elements are for a study of chemistry. *Rolf Siewing* defines "kind" according to two criteria [S6 p 172]:

1. *From the view of reproductive biology* a kind is a fertile community which exists under natural conditions and amongst whom unrestricted gene interchange is possible *(biospecies)*.

2. *From the structural viewpoint* a kind possesses the same constructional plan *(morphospecies)*.

EVOLUTION: In the evolutionary view all systematic categories are assumed to be related, and, consequently, that a phylogenetic tree exists. In setting up this tree, evolution is faced with an unresolvable problem. *Peters* and his co-authors (quoted in [G2 p 49]) concede that one cannot set up any reconstruction that is inherently plausible. Some yardstick for measuring its plausibility must be available. In any case we have a preordained theory, namely the theory of evolution. The circularity of this reasoning becomes clear: What has to be proved, has already been assumed to start with. The problem of evolutionary systematics, to trace unknown, untraceable relationships, is painted as follows by *Siewing* [S6 p 173]:

> "It is like an observer who views a flooded orchard with only the tips of the branches visible above the water. He does not know how these branches connect with one another, nor how they eventually connect with the tree trunks. The major part of evolution containing the gaps in the lines of descent, is hidden under water. These gaps must be bridged methodically."

SCIENTIFIC OBJECTIONS: The essential quantity in all life forms is the information contained in the genes. The presupposed evolutionary tree of descent (phylogenesis) is not controlled nor guided by information; thus it is an impossibility according to informatics theory [G9 p 16-17]. On the other hand, the development of embryos (ontogenesis) is a process which is controlled and guided by information. Recent discoveries in molecular biology have shown that very many mechanisms in living cells exist for the purpose of transferring exact information [S2]. This basic requirement for the constancy of the various kinds of organisms is conceded by *G Osche*, an evolutionary biologist [O2 p 53]:

> "The set of genes of an organism is a finely tuned team, a balanced 'genome' whose harmonious cooperation determines the orderly development of a living being. This finely balanced genome is extremely important for the organism, and is always transmitted unchanged at every single step of cell division and the division of cell nuclei and chromosomes. Before every cell division the genetic code must be replicated, in such a way that exactly the same chemically defined configuration is formed. This identical replication of the genes guarantees the constancy of genetic information. Roughly speaking, this replication is responsible for the phenomenon that storks always hatch from stork eggs with all the characteristics of this kind of bird."

Mutations and selection cannot be a source of new or different information (see OB17). The evolutionist assumption that simple construction plans could produce more complex plans by means of mutations and selection, is false according to information theory. No such event has ever been observed; on the contrary, the inverse is valid: The main result of heredity is to keep the distinguishing characteristics of all kinds of organisms constant. In the process of sexual reproduction new gene combinations are being formed continuously, so that every single individual has an unrepeatably unique set of genes. Mammals possess approximately one million genes. Such large quantities together with the very large number of possible combinations are the reason why no two persons are identical. The same holds for all bisexual organisms. Reproduction is only possible within fixed boundaries; it cannot take place outside these boundaries. With their definition of basic types, *Reinhard Junker* and *Siegfried Scherer* express a similar view [J2 p 207]:

> "All individuals who are directly or indirectly linked by cross-breeding, are regarded as belonging to one basic type, or whose germ cells, after actual fertilisation, at least begin to develop into an embryo having hereditary characteristics of both parents."

THE BIBLE: From the creation account it is clear that all living beings were created in clearly separate groups – each according to its kind. This concise formulation has some important results which totally repudiate the evolutionary view:

– Man as well as all the kinds of plants and animals were created separately. This excludes the possibility of phylogenetic relationships.

– The great number of reproductive mechanisms did not evolve, but they were created at the beginning: "Seed-bearing plants and trees on the land that bear fruit with seed in it, according to their various kinds" (Gen 1:11).

– Life did not begin as a single primordial cell from which all other life forms developed.

– The kinds form closed, complete groups. And there was also no primitive tree, no protofish, no first bird, and no primitive humanoids.

- The *"kinds"* mentioned in Genesis (Hebrew *"min"*; used only in singular!) could best be described as being similar to the basic types defined above. God created the original kinds with the ability to diversify into races.

5.3 Animal Nourishment (OB15)

EVOLUTION: The battle for nourishment is seen as one of the most important driving forces in the evolution of organisms. In the Darwinian view *"the survival of the fittest"* means that those individuals have a selective advantage who best survive the struggle of "eat or be eaten" in raw nature.

THE BIBLE: On the sixth creation day God determined what man and beast should eat:

> "Then God said, 'I give you every seed-bearing plant on the face of the whole earth and every tree that has fruit with seed in it. They will be yours for food. And to all the beasts of the earth and all the birds of the air and all the creatures that move on the ground – everything that has the breath of life in it – I give every green plant for food.' And it was so" (Gen 1:29-30).

Originally man and beast thus were vegetarian. No living being needed to be afraid of being eaten by another. Before sin entered the universe, there was complete harmony in all spheres of creation. Man's sin resulted in a catastrophe of such inconceivable magnitude that nobody today can form a picture of the previous "very good" creation. Can anyone imagine an earth with no death, neither pain nor disease, no predators or pests, no parasites, no robbery and no rivalry? In addition to the formation of very different ecosystems and relations, the changes in the animal world also involved drastic physiological modifications. Originally no animals were unclean or possessed murderous talons, claws or fangs, snakes did not have poison sacs, and all bacteria and viruses were benign. Whole families of animals became exclusively carnivorous. And only after the Noahic flood man was given permission to eat the meat of animals (Gen 9:3). This fatal transformation of creation is also described in the New Testament: "For the creation was subjected to frustration, not by its own choice, … We know that the whole creation has been groaning as in the pains of childbirth right up to the present time" (Rom 8: 20, 22). However, the time will come when God "will make a covenant" (Hos 2:20) with the animals and again let them live safely. Only after the results of sin have been removed from the earth, will the original state be seen again: "The wolf will live with the lamb, the leopard will lie down with the goat … the lion will eat straw like the ox. The infant will play near the hole of the cobra" (Isaiah 11:6-8). Then, as in the beginning, all animals will again be vegetarian.

The digestion of vegetable matter is an appreciably more complex process than the catabolism (breaking down) of meat proteins. According to evolution more complex processes and structures evolved from simpler ones, but also in this case the Bible bears quite a different witness.

5.4 Differences between Human Life and Animal Life (OB16)

EVOLUTION: Man is supposed to have descended directly from the animal kingdom by means of the same processes involving the same evolutionary factors which caused animals to evolve. For this reason the differences between man and beast are not regarded as fundamental, but as a difference in degree only. Man has only developed to a higher level. *Carsten Bresch* describes this view in his definition of evolution [B7 p 10]: "Evolution is defined as the development of all things in all spheres of our world – including the descent of man from apelike ancestors." The so-called proofs for evolution based on *homologies* emphasise the idea of descent from common ancestors.

SCIENTIFIC OBJECTIONS: Even on the purely biological plane there is a wide, unbridgeable chasm between man and beast, as illustrated by the following four considerations:

1. *The human brain* possesses qualities [G2 p 115-130] that have no parallel in the animal world. One consequence is man's explicit mental capabilities.

2. *Man possesses the faculty of speech* (see OB2), and his creative communication by means of his vocal system is completely different from those of animals [G7 p 112-130]. He has the unique ability to pay attention to various matters at will; he has an inconceivably wide range of interests and observation, because it is possible to consider spatially and temporally remote objects; he is able to make abstractions and to use his system of signs for metalingual purposes.

3. *Only man is fully bipedal;* he can walk upright because of the special structure of the spine. Thus our hands are not required for locomotion, and are available for other purposes.

4. *Only man is able to express emotions* (e.g. joy, sadness, hope, laughter, shyness). Some animals seem to have similar abilities, but they cannot be compared with human emotions.

THE BIBLE: The Bible clearly distinguishes between man and beast:

1. On the sixth day Adam was created *"in the image of God"* and quite apart from the land animals through a clearly distinguished separate act of creation. The Hebrew word *"bara"* (create) is used three times in Genesis 1:27 to emphasise this act of creation.

2. Only man received the breath of God. In this way he was given a spirit (Eccl 12:7; 1 Thess 5:23) so that he transcends the world of the animals.

3. Only when Adam was created, did God "use his hands": "And the Lord God formed (Hebrew *"yatsar"*) man from the dust of the ground and breathed into his nostrils the breath of life" (Gen 2: 7). In the Old Testament the Hebrew word *"yatsar"* is used to describe the actions of a potter who skilfully and imaginatively forms his vessels. In the same way God used earthly matter for Adam's physical parts.

4. Only man can actually communicate with God. Only he possesses the gift of speech and of prayer by means of which he can express all his thoughts before his Creator. Man was created to be near and close to God. He is dependent on communion with God.

5. Only man has a free will and possesses the faculty of creative thought. According to Psalm 8:6 man was made "a little lower than the heavenly beings." Human beings possess gifts such as freely developing personalities, inventiveness, and the capacity for cultural development (writing, music, historical awareness).

6. Even the difference in flesh is mentioned in the Bible: "All flesh is not the same: Men have one kind of flesh, animals have another, birds another and fish another" (1 Cor 15:39). This finding has consequences for molecular biology: Proteins comprise the major part of the body. The human body contains approximately fifty thousand different kinds of proteins, each fulfilling its own specific functions. They have different amino acid sequences. All organisms have certain amino acids in the same positions in the polypeptide chain, and they serve to establish and preserve the characteristic functions of the specific protein. In contrast to this precise

positioning there are other positions where the amino acids clearly differ from one kind to the other.

7. It is said only about man that he was not only created *"by God"*, but also *"for Him"* (Col 1:16). This high purpose is only ascribed to man. Animals are also creatures of God, but they did not receive the calling to become children of God (John 1:12).

8. In contrast to the animals, man is an eternal being; this means that his existence never ends, even after the death of the body (Luke 16:19-31). An imperishable body will be raised from the perishable one (1 Cor 15:42).

6. Observations on Information Science

The origin of life has always been a subject of speculation. The questions *"Whence? Why? and Whither?"* are directly involved. If our answer to "Whence?" is incorrect, then we will also be wrong about the purpose of life and the way to reach our destiny. Very many diverse and complex life forms exist, and even the simplest unicellular organism is so purposefully constructed and so much more complex than anything that man can invent or design. *B-O Küppers* regards the question of the origin of life as of equal significance as the problem of the origin of biological information [K4 p 250]. The present author can agree with this, but with the following reservation: The solution to the problem of the origin of biological information is unquestionably a necessary prerequisite for the clarification of the problem of the origin of life, even though it may not be a sufficient requirement. For this reason we devote a separate chapter to this topic.

6.1 What is Information? The View of Information Science (OB17)

The transfer of information is one of the fundamental principles of life. When insects carry pollen from one flower to another, it essentially comprises a transfer of information (genetic information); the actual substance being used, is unimportant. A general rule is that any piece of information that has to be transmitted, requires two conditions, namely

– a physical carrier for storage and for the control of processes and

- an unambiguously defined coding system for representing ideas in the form of symbols that can be copied.

We thus establish:

THEOREM 1: Physical carriers are necessary for the storage of information.

THEOREM 2: Every code is based on a volitional agreement.

The necessity of having a physical storage medium has deluded many to regard information as only a material entity. But it is clear from Theorem 2 that a code is an intellectual concept; the information conveyed by the code definitely has a mental character. All structural operating, and communication systems in a living organism are always based on a very effective coding system. The origin of these codes is fundamentally an unsolvable problem for evolution, because, although codes represent mental concepts, only material causes are considered. In evolutionary circles this problem is acknowledged, even though the causes of this dilemma are not mentioned. *J Monod* for instance, writes [M3 p 135]: "But the major problem is the origin of the genetic code and of its translation mechanism." Some of the fundamental theorems of the concept of information now follow (the author has discussed these extensively elsewhere [G3, G7, G9, G10]):

THEOREM 3: Several hierarchical levels characterise all information [G3, G7, G9, G10], namely syntax (code, grammar), semantics (meaning), pragmatics (action) and the apobetics level (teleological level, result, purpose). All these categories are structurally NON-MATERIAL.

THEOREM 4: Every piece of information implies the existence of a sender, and every piece of information is intended for a single recipient or for many receivers.

THEOREM 5: Information is inherently not a material entity, but a mental or spiritual one. Material processes do not qualify as sources of information.

72

Information is also essentially not a probabilistic concept, although one may study symbols from a statistical viewpoint (as in *Shannon's* theory). Information is always established by volition. Consequently three further theorems can be formulated:

THEOREM 6: Information is not a probabilistic entity.

THEOREM 7: Every piece of information requires a mental or spiritual source (a sender).

THEOREM 8: Information only originates voluntarily (intention, intuition, disposition). Stated differently: Every piece of information has a mental (intellectual or spiritual) source.

Theorems 6 to 8 lead to a fundamental theorem that excludes evolution by means of the mechanisms mutation and selection which are so frequently mentioned:

THEOREM 9: Mutation and selection cannot produce new information.

According to theorems 3, 7 and 8 information represents something that is mental or intellectual (semantics). This fact corners all evolutionary concepts, as is accepted by *B-O Küppers*:

> "A theory of the origin of life must necessarily include the origin of semantic information. And exactly here lies the basic difficulty of any theory of the origin of life. The fundamental empirical sciences in their traditional form exclude semantic phenomena from their intended range of application … The central question pertaining to the problem of the origin of life is therefore: To what extent can the concept of semantic information be made objective and become an object of study of a mechanistically oriented science as molecular biology is purported to be?"

When only material causes may be considered as in evolution, even as a source for information, then one has a point of departure which fails when it comes to the empirical laws of information science. Cyberneticist *D M McKay* describes such a viewpoint by saying that it is impossible to sail towards a beacon which we have nailed to the bow of our own ship.

Information may conveniently be differentiated into three groups according to purpose:

THEOREM 10: The origin of any construction is volitional and conceptual. The conceptual solution in the shape of *structural information* implies the presence of intelligence (an abundant supply of ideas).

THEOREM 11: *Operational information* is a necessary prerequisite for the preordained functioning of a system.

THEOREM 12: The *communication of information* requires an agreement between the sender and the recipient.

We can now summarise some of the important theorems which satisfy scientific criteria S7 and S11:

1. There can be no information without a code.

2. There can be no information without a sender.

3. There can be no information without a mental (spiritual) source.

4. There can be no information without volition.

5. All information comprises five hierarchical levels (statistic, syntactic, semantic, pragmatic, and apobetic)

6. There is no such thing as random information.

6.2   What is Information? The Biblical View (OB18)

The aspects of information that we studied above, are also found in the Bible:

1. *Code is based on mutual agreement (the syntactic aspect):* Any code depends on a free and volitional agreement whereby different sets of symbols are made to correspond with one another, or single symbols are given a meaning. This underlies all types of codes (e. g. hieroglyphics, Morse code, various alphabets, and EDP codes). The Bible tells of symbolic meanings set up by God. The mark given to Cain was a *sign of protection* (Gen 4:15). After the flood the rainbow was designated as a *sign of the covenant* that God made with Noah: "Never again will the waters become a flood to destroy all life" (Gen 9:15). The blood on the doorframes of the Israelites in Egypt was also a *sign to protect* the firstborn from death (Exodus 12:13). The bread and the wine taken at holy communion are *signs of remembrance* of the death of Jesus, and of the consequent salvation of believers.

2. *Language as carrier of meaning (semantic aspect):* The transfer of information is identical to the communication of meaningful content. For this purpose a suitable language is required. This holds for all technical, biological or communicative information. This is clearly expressed in 1 Corinthians 14:10-11: "Undoubtedly there are many languages in the world, yet none of them is without meaning. If then I do not grasp the meaning of what someone is saying, I am a foreigner to him, and he is a foreigner to me."

3. *Information requires action (pragmatic aspect):* "Therefore everyone who hears these words of mine and puts them into practice, is like a wise man who built his house on the rock" (Matt 7:24).

4. *Information sets an aim (apobetical aspect):* "… whoever hears my word (semantics) and believes Him who sent me (pragmatic), has eternal life and will not be condemned; he has crossed over from death to life (teleological aspect)" (John 5:24).

6.3   What is Life? The Evolutionary View

Evolutionists regard life as an exclusively material process. In this vein *B-O Küppers* mentions four necessary criteria for the existence of life [K3 p 53-55]:

- The ability to procreate
- The ability to mutate
- The ability of metabolic interchanges (change)
- The ability to evolve in the *Darwinian* sense.

The presuppositional role of evolution is immediately clear (see basic assumption E1). It is thus not strange that an evolutionist straitjacket exists in connection with the origin of life. This leads to the following conclusion:

> Life is purely a material process and it is therefore possible to describe it in physico-chemical terms. It differs from inanimate nature only in its complexity.

From this point of departure it is therefore possible to study the origin of life, as for example *Hans Kuhn* sees it [K5 p 838-839]: "The hypothesis that the origin of life was a physico-chemical process that necessarily had to happen under certain conditions, is our point of departure ... We expect that (through random variations) self-organising and self-replicating systems will blindly and automatically arise, and our aim is to understand how the known genetic equipment came into existence during the available time of earth's history." At the beginning of the twentieth century *Ernst Haeckel* was so carried away by his evolutionist euphoria that he told *Emil H Fischer*, a chemical scientist who studied proteins [W1 p 82]: "Stick to your researches, some day they will begin to crawl." In the same vein *Friedrich Engels* defined life as "the special form in which protein particles exist." *M Eigen* regards life as a hyper cycle, and *G and H von Wahlert* reduce it to simply

[W1 p 79]: "… an organised condition of matter." In contrast to the time before *Darwin*, life was regarded quite differently after his time [W1 p 73]: "*Darwin* changed spiritual man into the product of a materialistic development." Nevertheless, *Kuhn* hopes to overcome the intellectual problems regarding such a reductionism [K3 p 838]: "The deeply ingrained perception that a system as complex as the genetic equipment could never have been produced by chance, and that the origin of living organisms was a physico-chemical phenomenon, had a strong influence on philosophical thought. The present work is an attempt to overcome this psychological problem."

The evolutionistic definition of life leads to the simple formula:

$$\text{LIFE} = \text{complex matter} = \text{a function of (chemistry + physics)} \qquad (L1)$$

The well-known evolutionistic biologist *E Mayr* bemoans the fact that especially scientists in the exact sciences are not willing to accept such materialism [M1 p 395]: "The objection most frequently raised against evolution during the past century, was that the theory was materialistic … the most exact scientists, the physicists and mathematicians, try to point out the inadequacies of evolution. When I addressed a small group in Copenhagen, *Niels Bohr* expressed his strong doubts. Since then this doubt even became the topic of scientific conferences." Indeed: The number of doubters on scientific grounds is increasing steadily. For many years a new science, **informatics**, has progressively been growing in importance. From this vantage point completely new insights into the true nature of life emerged. *E Jantsch* believed [J1 p 411] that natural history, including the history of man, could be regarded as the history of the organisation of matter and energy. But our point of departure in the next section is that information is a central factor of all life forms.

6.4 What is Life? The Informational View (OB19)

Matter and energy are necessary aspects of living forms, but they do not fundamentally distinguish between living and inanimate systems. "Information" is however a basic characteristic of all sentient beings. This does not mean that life has now been explained, but a very important factor has been mentioned. Even at the lowest level, in the case of viroids, which are simpler than viruses, where we have single molecules of nucleic acid, information is the distinguishing entity. Without a doubt the most complex information processing system is a human being. Even when applying the theorems mentioned initially, we can now formulate a further equation, L2, contrasting with L1:

LIFE = material part (physical and chemical aspects) + non-material part (information having an intellectual source)   (L2)

This formula comprises a radical extension over and against basic assumption E3 of evolution, but even L2 is not sufficient, because it cannot explain all life phenomena (as for example the shaping of bodily growth; consciousness, and responsibility). This author introduced three classes of information which are present in sentient organisms [in G7 p 136-139]:

1. *Structural information:* Although not sufficient for explaining the origin of an organism, genetic information is essential. It contains the individual constructional blueprint for every life form, and ensures its effective transmission from generation to generation. In every grain of wheat it is responsible for the growth of a new plant that in its turn produces wheat grains as seed. In the same way the merging of male sperm cells and female ova determines the genetic combination of the new person. The embryo cannot develop without the accompanying constructional information. This speci-

fic information is decisive for the development of the appropriate structures, even if it is not sufficient. By using only a few similar building blocks (20 amino acids), the programme determines whether an oak, a rose, a butterfly, a swallow, a horse, or a man is constructed. The most important part of transfering the genotype, is not the essential material interest, but the information within and this is non-material.

2. *Operational information:* In all the different kinds of life forms there is an immense variety of information processing systems that drive the internal "operational" processes:

   – All the required operational and structural materials must be synthesised inside the cells. In the human body alone, fifty thousand different proteins have to be built up according to exact chemical and procedural requirements. If the specifications of only one of these proteins are absent from the controlling programme, it could be dangerous or lethal (e. g. insulin).

   – The nervous system serves as the communication network for all relevant information for controlling the harmonious operation of all organic systems, as well as for controlling the movements of the limbs.

   – Hormones carry chemical messages for controlling certain growth processes and for the activation of numerous physiological functions.

3. *Communicative information:* Communication, especially with others of the same kind, plays a central role in the life of organisms. For this purpose systems for the transmission and reception of signals exist which certainly comprise some of the most amazing features of creation. In the animal kingdom communication systems essentially serve the following purposes: Sexual

courtship (e. g. the mating calls of birds, and the sexual secretions of insects), communicating a source of food (bee dances), detection of enemies (the pheromones of ants), the sharing of tasks among families or colonies (like ants and bees), and for befriending other organisms (ants appease the caterpillars of the butterfly "Blue" by allomones). The variety and sensitivity of the various receptors are astounding. Some quantitative examples:

– Certain grasshoppers can detect soil vibrations having an amplitude of only $5 \cdot 10^{-10}$ cm. That is 1/25 of the diameter of the first electron orbit of a hydrogen atom.

– The threshold of audibility of the human ear is 10^{-12} Watt per square metre. By this it reaches the physically possible limits.

– The heat-sensitive organ (pit organ) of the Malayan moccasin snake can detect a change in temperature of 1/1000 °C, independent of the temperature of its own body.

– Even a single molecule of the pheromone bombykol secreted by the female bombyx mori can still be detected by the male's antenna. In this respect one should remember that one cubic centimetre of air contains $26.9 \cdot 10^{18}$ molecules (or nearly 27 million billion).

Human speech is distinctly different from all animal communication systems. Articulated speech is a very versatile instrument which not only serves to convey meaning, but it is the foundation of all our thoughts and mental activities. The German language employs more than half a million words and it is impossible to calculate the number of possible combinations of the numerous forms of the words into sentences and paragraphs that our power of speech is capable of. The number of expressible thoughts is also exceedingly large. No animal communication system possesses such creative possibilities; they can only be used for strictly limited, "burnt in" forms of expression.

Nearly all information processes are controlled by the brain. It is the most complex but also the least understood organ. Most biological functions cannot proceed without the brain. If the brain is dead, then the whole organism also dies (cerebral death; compare OB5).

All these information systems require an intellectual source according to the information theorems mentioned above. The endeavours of evolutionists to explain life as a purely mechanistic phenomenon, gloss over these facts and ignore these verifiable theorems.

6.5   What is Life? The Biblical View (OB20)

Up to this point we emphasised that *information* is an essential characteristic of life. The realisation that information is an intellectual entity, saves us from regarding life as purely mechanistic. But the essentials of life have not yet been fully encompassed, as can immediately be realised from the following: At the moment of death the totality of DNA information is still present in all the cells, but the operational and communication information has disappeared. It is thus clear that there is another crucial difference between living beings and dead organisms which cannot be found in the material domain. *Gilbert Ryle* described this aspect as follows [D1 p 79]:

> "Though the human body is an engine, it is not quite an ordinary engine, since some of its workings are governed by another engine inside it – this interior governor-engine being one of a very special sort. It is invisible, inaudible and it has no size or weight. It cannot be taken to bits and the laws it obeys are not those known to ordinary engineers."

81

He has addressed the soul of man which is part of his non-material being (see also OB8). It cannot be tested physically or chemically, but reveals itself in the nature of man, particularly in his free will (discussed more fully in [G2 p 190-194]). We have repeatedly emphasised that the origin of the non-material part of man can also be ascribed to the Creator. The following formulation can now be established along biblical lines:

THEOREM: No life can exist outside the will of God.

Equation L3 which clearly surpasses L2, can now be deduced from Biblical testimony:

LIFE = material part (structural appearance) +
non-material part 1 (= the structural, operational, and communication information encoded by God)
+ non-material part 2 (= soul, spirit)   (L3)

This formula points beyond scientifically researchable possibilities. As point of departure the basic evolutionary assumptions E3 and E5 have thus proved to be false.

6.6   The Origin of Biological Information and of Life

Paul Davies states [D1 p 61]: "Atoms do not need to be 'animated' to yield life, they simply have to be arranged in the appropriate complex way." This mechanistic reduction is inappropriate in view of the information "installed" in living organisms. This deficiency in the evolutionary model is acknowledged by *H Kuhn* [K5 p 838]: "It is not clear how the first biological systems could have developed ... they must already have possessed a mechanism which operated like the finely tuned genetic apparatus of present-day organisms. How could such systems have originated? Are the laws of physical chemistry sufficient for understanding such a process, or should we postulate further unknown principles?" As long as an intelligent source of information is excluded, people will try to invent the "perpetuum mobile of information". This is exactly what *B-O Küppers* attempted in his book with the highly promising title "Der Ursprung biologischer Information" (The origin of biological information [K4]). In stead of a consistently scientific treatment which would have brought him to the primary spiritual (mental) source of all information, he practises a natural "*molecular-Darwinistic*" philosophy. The following counter arguments can be raised against his exposition:

1. *Küppers* concedes that man-made artefacts (Latin "*arte factum*" = artificially made) are always preplanned for a specific purpose and use. He affirms that "we do not postulate any final purpose for natural objects" (p 34). But this is refuted by the presence in living organisms of highly purposeful organs and mechanisms like the brain, the limbs, internal organs, effectively controlled protein synthesis, sensory systems, and systems for the transmission of information.

2. *Küppers* ignores two fundamental empirically established theorems (see theorems 3 and 4):

   – "Every piece of information has a teleological (apobetic) aspect" (Greek "*apóbainon*" = result, consequence, source, purpose)

   – "Every piece of information implies that it has been transmitted by an intelligent source."

3. On the one hand *Küppers* acknowledges that every complex operational process requires a plan: "… we now know that a definite meticulous plan underlies the process of metabolism" (p 36), but, on the other hand, he ignores exactly the One Who originally specified this informationally controlled plan. At another place he stumbles on a crucial characteristic of information, without thinking it through: "One can only speak of in-

formation with respect to a sender and a recipient. Symbols are required for the establishment and transmission of information ..., recognition of these symbols requires a prearranged semantic agreement between the sender and the recipient" (p 62). He comes very close to the conclusion that information is an intellectual entity and thus requires a spiritual source. But his philosophical predisposition prevents him from realising this.

4. In his *"molecular-Darwinistic"* approach *Küppers* mistakenly regards information as a material entity, contrary to the empirically established results 2, 3, 5, 7, 8, and 10. *Norbert Wiener*, the well-known cyberneticist, had already pointed out that information could not be a physical entity: "Information is information, neither matter nor energy. Any materialism that does not accept this, cannot survive today."

5. Furthermore, there are no empirical results which support the *Küppers* model or indicate that information could originate by itself in the realm of molecules. His views therefore carry no scientific weight, but are merely a philosophical-mental construct having no connection with reality.

6. On pages 126-136 of his book referred to above *Küppers* describes a computer simulation which purports to demonstrate that a certain target word could, by means of a selection mechanism, "evolve" from an initial sequence of letters. Evolution has no place for goals to strive to, but in this case the target word has been prearranged. In this way the molelucular-Darwinistic point of departure reduced itself "ad absurdum". And again we have shown that information cannot originate by itself. The anticipated result has been prearranged.

From these discussions it should again become clear that all efforts to explain an origin of information depending on matter alone, fail empirically. We thus turn to another source which is unknown to and actively rejected by evolutionists, namely the witness of the Bible:

The intellectual source for all information as required by information theory, including biological information, is already mentioned on the first page of the Bible: "In the beginning GOD created ..." (Gen 1:1).

Further revelations in the New Testament persistently emphasise that Christ is the Creator (John 1:1-4 & 10; Col 1:15-17; Hebr 1:1-2). Any theory of origins, whether evolutionistic or even creationistic, which does not include Christ, must inevitably lead to false conclusions. Per definition atheistic evolution leads away from Christ, and theistic evolution which provides a place for God or some other deity, is similarly unable to explain the origin of life, because the essential role of Christ as Creator is excluded from consideration. In Colossians 2:3 the New Testament describes Jesus Christ as the Source of all the treasures of wisdom and knowledge; He is therefore also the Source of all biological information. Similarly John's distinctive introductory words uniquely identify the information source with Jesus, the incarnate Word of God: "In the beginning was the Word, and the Word was with God, and the Word was God ... Through Him all things were made; without Him nothing was made that has been made ... He was in the world, and ... the world was made through Him ..." (John 1:1, 3, & 10). The theorems mentioned above, in particular 5, 7 and 8, are thus confirmed in the Bible, because the information found in biological systems requires a really brilliant Initiator of ideas. New information can only originate through a creative thought process. Understanding, wisdom, planning, and profound thoughts mutually imply one another, and they are synonyms for the present-day concepts intelligence and information.

The Bible expresses this relationship in many ways:

Proverbs 3:19:
"By wisdom the LORD laid the earth's foundations, by understanding He set the heavens in place."

Psalm 40:5:
"Many, O LORD my God, are the wonders You have done. The things You planned ..."

Psalm 104:24:
"How many are Your works, O LORD! In wisdom You made them all; the earth is full of Your creatures."

All these affirmations make it clear that Christ is not only the Prime Source of all biological information, but He is also the Creator of all life. When this answer is accepted, then all evolutionist concepts about the origin of life prove to be false.

7. Progressive Evolution or Complete Creation?

EVOLUTION: The entire cosmos, our earth and all life forms resulted from an extremely slow process of development from the simple to the complex, from barely structured to higher forms of organisation, from inanimate to animate, and from low life forms to higher levels. All organisms can be arranged in a line of descent and development right up to man. According to the evolutionary view this process is still continuing. All earlier living organisms were merely temporary forms of life at that moment, and present-day individuals should then be regarded as half-way stations for future developments (see evolutionary assumption E11). In this respect *Wuketits* believes that evolution as such has not stopped [W7 p 275]. "It seems justified to expect new kinds and new degrees of differentiation to appear." The following quotations confirm the assumption of continuing evolution in various areas:

1. *Continuing cosmic evolution:* "Not only life, but also the entire cosmos went through a process of development. Beginning with a singularity of immense density and temperature and with the 'big bang'. The universe assumed its present form after a development lasting approximately 15 thousand million years" [*R Siewing* [S6 p XIX]). In the evolutionary view this process has definitely not been completed. An extremely distant stage of development is described by *R Breuer* [B8 p 51]: "The sun, together with the earth, may eventually be ejected from our galaxy. Then, in the dark isolation of intergalactic space the earth will have all the time in the world to fall in slow motion into the black hole that had once been the sun. At this time, after 10^{20} years, the classical

evolution of the cosmos would end." *S Weinberg* justifiably referred to the "dark cloud of great uncertainty" that looms over such a cosmological model.

2. *Continuing biological evolution:* "Man and beast can no longer be seen as … completed creatures of a paradisiacal six-day activity. But the kinds originated during long epochs of earth's history, one after the other, fulfilling themselves and changing, dying out or branching off in new directions from an upwardflowing current aspiring to the organic perfection of living matter. Eventually the present diversity of forms developed" (*J Illies* [I2 p 33]).

3. *Continuing human evolution:* "At the moment we are the apex reached by the great constructors of changing kinds on earth, we are 'state of the art', but certainly not their last word … If I had to regard man as the final image of God, then this view of God would drive me insane. But when I realise that our recent ancestors (in terms of the history of the earth) were very ordinary monkeys, closely related to chimpanzees, then I catch a glimmer of hope. It does not require undue optimism to assume that something better and higher may yet develop from us humans … The long sought for missing link between animals and real human beings – are we!" (*K Lorenz* [L2 p 215-216]).

THE BIBLE: The entire cosmos with all its countless stars, all basic types of life, as well as man, were created directly by God in one week, as described in Genesis. The whole of creation was finished and complete. All biological changes that occurred since that time, only resulted in diversification within the original kinds (e. g. the origin of races).

We read in Genesis 2:2 that "By the seventh day God had finished the work He had been doing; so on the seventh day He rested from all His work." And in Hebrews 4:3: "And yet His work has been finished since the creation of the world."

8. The Consequences of Theistic Evolution

8.1 Danger No 1: Denial of Central Biblical Teachings

1. *The Bible as authoritative source of information:* The entire Bible bears witness that we are dealing with a source of truth authored by God. The Old Testament (OT) prophets took this position (e. g. Isaiah 1:10; Jer 7:1; and Hos 4:6) as well as the New Testament (NT) apostles (e. g. 2 Tim 3:16; and 2 Peter 1:21). *H W Beck* concludes from archaeological researches [B1 p 39]: "The hypothesis of a long oral tradition and of a long evolution of literary developmental processes is really not probable." The apostles not only knew the Scriptures exceedingly well, but the deeper meanings were also disclosed to them by the Holy Spirit. Jesus Christ revealed certain information to Paul, as a chosen instrument of God (Gal 1:12), and Paul confessed unequivocally: "I *believe everything* that … is written" (Acts 24:14). Peter affirmed that he did not follow cleverly invented stories, but was an eye-witness (2 Peter 1:16). The special key to understanding Scripture, is given by God's Son Himself. Jesus states that His words will never pass away (Matt 24:35). He guarantees that *everything* that has been written, will be fulfilled (Luke 18:31). He authorised all the meaningful elements of the text of the Bible (e. g. Luke 16:17) and confirmed that all biblical accounts described real historical events, for example the creation of the first human couple (Matt 19:4-5), the universality of the flood and the destruction of *all* air-breathing creatures (Matt 24:38-39), and the history of Jonah (Matt 12:40-41). The

present author discusses the authority of the Bible more fully in [G6].

2. *The relation between the Old and the New Testament:* Many statements of the OT are quoted in the NT, but the latter is much more than merely a commentary on the OT. It is the fulfilment of the Old Testament: "These (the people of the OT) were all commended for their faith, yet none of them received what had been promised. God had planned something better for us ..." (Hebr 11:39-40). Everything was consummated in Christ. The OT is the indispensable "ramp" leading up to the NT, as in the case of a motor freeway. Jesus says of the OT: "You diligently study the Scriptures because you think that by them you possess eternal life. These are the Scriptures that testify about me" (John 5:39). The NT reveals many things for the first time; it is new. The OT can only really be understood from the NT, because the former refers to Christ. This principle was disclosed by Jesus to the disciples on their way to Emmaus. The OT is regarded as authoritative, right up to the requirements of the Law fulfilled by Christ (Hebr 9:10) and the practices around sacrifices (Hebr 10:1b & 4).

3. *The creation account – literal or poetic:* It is often said that we cannot really understand God's creative acts. This sounds humble and at first sight even commendable. It is however false, since it contradicts God's will that we must accept His Word in real earnest (Jer 22:29; John 8:47; 2 Tim 1:13). We should rather be thankful for all the information given to us in Genesis and numerous other passages. The reasons given below should make it clear that the biblical creation account should not be regarded as a myth, neither as a parable, nor allegorically, but as a report:

   – Biological, astronomical and anthropological facts are given in a didactical form.

- As is customary for present-day measuring techniques, the appropriate methods for measuring the physical time units "day" and "year" are given (Gen 1:14).

- In the Ten Commandments God bases the six working days and one day of rest on the same time span as that described in the creation account (Exodus 20:8-11).

- In the NT Jesus frequently refers to facts of creation (e. g. Matt 19:4-5).

- Nowhere in the Bible are there any indications that the creation account should be understood in any other way than as a factual report.

The doctrine of theistic evolution vehemently tries to undermine this basic way of reading the Bible as vouched for by Jesus, the prophets and the apostles. Events reported in the Bible are reduced to mythical imagery, and an understanding of the message of the Bible as being true in word and meaning, is scorned and regarded as superstitious. *H von Ditfurth* writes in the same vein [D3 p 295-296]:

"The literal meaning of the mythical imagery with which theologians proclaim their message, bears no relation to the contents of the message. They were not even valid 2000 years ago, when these images came into existence as expression of a living faith ... That was two millennia ago, so it doesn't hold for us any more. The semantic 'overtones' of the cultural matrix at the time of Christ's birth have long since been forgotten. At that time the mythical formulas were impressed on the philosophy and customs of the Judaic-Roman world ... Today we only have the skeleton, the bare framework of words and sentences, which fills us with respect and awe as an echo of the time when they originated. The real meanings and significance they once had, have long since been lost … Where mythical statements are reduced to their bare literal meaning, it becomes superstition."

Supporters of theistic evolution are found amongst critical theologians and philosophers (e. g. *C Westermann, G Altner, C F von Weizsäcker, T de Chardin*) and even some evangelical authors *(J Illies, H Rohrbach)*. Views based on a direct understanding of the Bible are scornfully regarded as "fundamentalistic" (e. g. *J Illies* [I3 p 43], *H von Ditfurth* [D3 p 306]). Adherence to the views of theistic evolution leads to the abandonment of central biblical teachings, and thus to disobedience towards God. The Bible warns against this:

1 Sam 15:23b:
"Because you have rejected the word of the LORD, he has rejected you …"

Acts 13:46b:
"Since you reject it (the word of God) and do not consider yourselves worthy of eternal life, …"

8.2 Danger No 2: Misrepresentation of the Nature of God

Jesus reveals God to us as our Father in Heaven Who is absolutely perfect (Matt 5:48), and the angels proclaim: "Holy, holy, holy is the LORD Almighty" (Isaiah 6:3). God is omnipotent (Gen 17:1); He is "the Father of the heavenly lights, who does not change" (James 1:17). The first epistle of John mentions three fundamental aspects of God's nature:

– God is love (1 John 4:16)

– God is light (1 John 1:5)

– God is life (Ps 36:10; 1 John 1:1-2)

As the Son of God Jesus is the true God and the everlasting Life (1 John 5:20). Through Him God made the universe (Heb 1:2). He is "gentle and humble in heart" (Matt 11:29), and "in Him is no sin" (1 John 3:5). If a God with these characteristics creates something, then His works could only be perfect (Deut 32:4) and very good (Gen 1:31).

The Darwinistic principle of *"the survival of the fittest"* means that the superior organisms will win the battle for survival and the unadapted ones will be weeded out. As a method for creating life forms, this procedure is totally contrary to the nature of Jesus the Creator.

In evolution progress is bought by pain and death. Improvement of species took place "over the dead bodies of individuals", as stated by *C F von Weizsäcker. Hans Sachsse* affirms regretfully and accusingly that one could not escape the conclusion that everything is not as it should be [S1 p 51]: "The way of 'development' entailed an appalling measure of pain and sorrow. What we discern in evolution, is not only wonderful, but also gruesome. Death is evolution's strategy for elevating life." The biblical testimony concerning God's nature is distorted when death and ghastliness are presumed to be creative principles. *Wolfgang Böhme*, a theologian who supports theistic evolution, even goes so far as to say that he regards sin as a harmless evolutionary factor [B5 p 89-90]:

> "If development has to march forward, sin is a marginal phenomenon at the edge of the great process of evolution, perhaps even a necessary feature. Nature cannot sin. Can man then be sinful when he is merely a product of nature, a link in the chain of nature's creatures, taken from the earth to which he must someday return? *Teilhard de Chardin* expressed the opinion that sin was a necessary factor in evolution, that it was the 'risk' and the 'shadow'

which accompany all creative events … The myth
of man's fall into sin is found in the beginning of
the Bible."

This approach is one small step from an arrogant accusation of God:

"How can … God be exonerated when He created
a world filled with suffering of all imaginable
kinds – pain and fear and illness? How did evil enter the world when it is God's creation? … all believers must consider the question of how the ailments of the world can be reconciled with God's
omnipotence" *(H von Ditfurth* [D3 p 145]).

The anti-biblical consequences of theistic evolution have
become clear from the above quotations:

- a false representation of God and of Christ
- God is seen as imperfect
- death and ghastliness are ascribed to the Creator as
  principles of creation
- it is assumed that the holy God used sin to create life
- sin is regarded as a harmless evolutionary factor, causing Jesus Christ's work of redemption as the only possibility of man's salvation, to appear (nearly) absurd
- Adam's fall into sin is seen as a myth instead of reality,
  conveying a false impression of death and suffering in
  this world.

8.3   Danger No 3: Loss of the Key for Finding God

The Bible describes man as being completely ensnared by
sin after Adam's fall: "For what I do, is not the good I
want to do; no, the evil I do not want to do – this I keep on
doing" (Rom 7:19). Only those who understand this fact,
ask the appropriate question: "What a wretched man I

am! Who will rescue me from this body of death?" (Rom 7:24). Only those persons who realise that they are sinful and lost, will seek the Saviour. Jesus briefly formulated the reason for His mission to this world as follows: "The Son of man came to save what was lost" (Matt 18:11). Only as sinners can we find the way to God: "Father, I have sinned against heaven and against you" (Luke 15:21). Anyone who has unburdened his sins under the cross of Jesus, can joyfully cry out after being set free: "Thanks be to God – through Jesus Christ our Lord!" (Rom 7:25).

Evolution knows no sin in the biblical sense of missing one's purpose (in relation to God). Sin is made meaningless, and that is exactly the opposite of what the Holy Spirit does – He declares sin to be sinful. *J Illies* sees aggression as the flywheel that actually set evolution in motion. He regards the fist as the active instrument and proof of becoming human. *Hans Mohr* regards murder, hate and aggression as the "eggshells of evolution" (see OB 9), the prerequisites without which man could not have developed. If sin is seen in this way, then one has lost the key for finding God. The Bible affirms that "All wrongdoing is sin" (1 John 5:17), and if the pardon through the Son of God is disregarded, then "you are still in your sins" (1 Cor 15:17). Adherence to the doctrine of evolution conceals the real nature of sin and leads one astray: "If we claim to be without sin, we deceive ourselves and the truth is not in us" (1 John 1:8). Jesus once told people who held this view, "that you would die in your sins" (John 8:24). *The conclusion is inevitable:* There is no support for theistic evolution in the Bible.

8.4 Danger No 4: God's Incarnation becomes Incidental

The incarnation of God through His Son Jesus Christ is one of the basic teachings of the Bible. The apostle John testifies: "The Word became flesh and lived for a while among us" (John 1:14). Although He was God, He "made himself nothing, taking the very nature of a servant, being made in human likeness. And being found in appearance as a man ..." (Phil 2:7-8). He became a human being to bring salvation to us. He is the only Mediator between God and men, the man Christ Jesus" (1 Tim 2:5). The idea of evolution undermines this foundation of our salvation. *Hoimar von Ditfurth* discusses the incompatibility of Jesus's incarnation with evolutionary thought [D3 p 21-22]:

> "Consideration of evolution inevitably forces us to a critical review ... of Christian formulations. This clearly holds for the central Christian concept of the 'incarnation' of God ... The absoluteness with which the event in Bethlehem has up to now been regarded in Christian philosophy, is contrary to the identification of this man who personifies this event (= Jesus), with man having the nature of homo sapiens ... The only way that I see of resolving the contradiction (between evolution and the incarnation of Jesus) is to ascribe a basic historical relativity to the person Jesus Christ."

Von Ditfurth continues by saying that Jesus could not be a universal mediator between God and man, because neither the Neanderthal people (regarded as our probable ancestors), nor our potential descendants could or will understand Jesus. It now becomes clear that theistic evolution has allowed a profound loss of meaning and substance to enter.

The Bible commands us to test the spirits to determine whether they come from God. The criterion given in 1 John 4:2-3 helps us to size up theistic evolution: "This is how you can recognise the Spirit of God: Every spirit that acknowledges that Jesus Christ has come in the flesh, is from God, but every spirit that does not acknowledge

Jesus, is not from God. This is the spirit of the anti-christ, which you have heard is coming and even now is already in the world."

8.5 Danger No 5: Relativation of Jesus's Work of Redemption

The first man's fall into sin was a real event and is the direct cause of sin in this world; everybody else became tainted: "Therefore, just as sin entered the world through one man, and death through sin, and in this way death came to *all* men, because *all* have sinned ... Nevertheless, death reigned from the time of Adam ..." (Rom 5:12-13). In the New Testament Adam is explicitly named as the first man (1 Cor 15:45; 1 Tim 2:13). Theistic evolution does not acknowledge Adam as the first man; neither that he was created directly by God. The creation account is regarded as merely a mythical tale and nothing more than that. Jesus's work of redemption is relativised in the same way, because the sinner Adam and the Saviour Jesus are linked together in the Bible:

> "The judgment followed one sin (Adam's) and brought condemnation, but the gift followed many trespasses and brought justification. For if, by the trespass of the one man, death reigned through that one man, how much more will those who receive God's abundant provision of grace and of the gift of righteousness, reign in life through one man, Jesus Christ. Consequently, just as the result of one trespass was condemnation for all men, so also the result of one act of righteousness was justification that brings life for all men" (Rom 5:16-18).

If one does not regard Adam as a real historical person but as a mythical figure, then one can consequently not accept Jesus's work of redemption as real. This is exactly what is meant by *E Jantsch* when he says [J1 p 412]: "Humanity will not be saved by a god, but we will save ourselves." In this way theistic evolution conceals the glorious light of the Gospel (2 Cor 4:4) through which man's deliverance is accomplished.

8.6   Danger No 6: God becomes a God of the Gaps

The Bible states that God is the Prime Cause of all things: "Yet for us there is but one God, from whom all things came and for whom we live; and there is but one Lord, Jesus Christ, through whom all things came and through whom we live" (1 Cor 8:6). God thus created everything through Christ, as is emphasised even more in other passages (John 1:3; Col 1:15-17; Hebr 1:3). Whether or not we understand the scientific details of creation around us from the viewpoint of physics, chemistry, biology, astronomy, physiology, or information science, all phenomena are His handiwork and embody His ideas (Col 2:3).

The striking title of *J Illies'* book *"Der Jahrhundertirrtum"* (The delusion of the century) may raise the expectation that Darwinism is denied in favour of the biblical account of creation. But, amazingly, one is disillusioned by a firm confession of evolution [I4 p 188]: "The mountains and lakes of this earth are there for all to see; in a similar sense evolution is not a theory ... The transformation of the animal and plant world during the course of the epochs of earth's history towards continually higher forms, until eventually man himself developed in an uninterrupted chain from generation to generation, is just as visible a fact for the biological specialist (but only when he thinks in an evolutionary manner! – author) as the existence of mountains and lakes is for the geographer." Evolution is thus regarded as a fact. But *Illies* acknowledges that the evolutionary factors, mutation, selection and isolation, are unable to pass across the boundaries separating the various kinds: "Nobody, even if he has many millions of years at his disposal, can run peas and lentils through a screen and obtain beans" (p 57). Now theistic evolution reaches the point where God is "switched on".

The atheistic formula for evolution is:

EVOLUTION = matter + evolutionary factors (chance and necessity + mutation + selection + isolation + death) + very long time periods

In the theistic evolution view, God is added:

THEISTIC EVOLUTION = matter + evolutionary factors (chance and necessity + mutation + selection + isolation + death) + very long time periods + GOD

In this system God is not the omnipotent Lord of all things whose Word has to be taken seriously by all men, but He is integrated into the evolutionary philosophy. The only workspace allotted to Him is that part which evolution cannot explain with the means at its disposal. In this way He is reduced to being a "god of the gaps" for those phenomena about which there are doubts. In such a conceptual structure "God's housing shortage" (as *E Haeckel* called it) becomes steadily more acute. Theistic evolution deviates from the biblical concept of God, and this view has recently become all-important. *E Jantsch* describes a god who himself has become evolution [J1 p 412]: *"Hans Jonas grandly formulated this evolutionary concept of God by saying that again and again He gave himself up in a sequence of evolutionary developments. He transformed himself in this immersion with all the risks caused by uncertainty and free will in the interplay of evolutionary processes. God is therefore not absolute, but He himself has evolved – He is evolution."* It is clear that all man-made concepts of God are fundamentally false if terminology like the "God of evolution", the "God of the philosophers", or the "God of the physicists" is used. In this respect the commandment of the living God of the Bible, the Father of Jesus Christ, is highly significant: "You shall have no other gods besides Me" (Exodus 20:3).

8.7 Danger No 7: Loss of Biblical Chronology

The Bible provides us with a time-scale for history. Although not measured by means of atomic clocks, the following dates and facts underlay a proper understanding of the Bible:

– The time-scale cannot be extended indefinitely into the past, nor into the future. There is a well-defined beginning in Genesis 1:1, as well as a moment (Rev 10:6) when physical time will end (discussed more fully in [G5 p 23-31]).

– The earth and all other astronomical bodies are of the same age, except for the three-day difference reported in creation week.

– The total duration of creation was six days (Exodus 20:11)

– The age of the universe may be estimated in terms of the genealogies recorded in the Bible (note that it cannot be calculated exactly.) It is of the order of a few thousand years, and not at all in a range of millions or even thousands of millions of years.

– Galatians 4:4 points out the most outstanding event in the world's history: "But when the time had fully come, God sent His Son." The first coming of Jesus happened nearly 2000 years ago.

– The last phase of the present world's history which will end at the Second Coming of Jesus, began on the day of Pentecost (Acts 2:17).

– The coming of Christ in power and glory is the greatest expected event lying ahead. The exact date is unknown, because "the day of the Lord will come as a thief in the night" (1 Thess 5:2). Jesus has however mentioned certain definite signs (Matt 24) which will precede His Second Coming. From these we know that this time is near – much closer than ever before.

The long time periods in the past and in the future, as seen by evolutionists (compare OB10 and OB11), differ widely from the biblical time-scale. They also ignore the events prophesied for the time of the end. While the Bible draws our attention to the coming of the Lord and to the temporal limits of this world (its impermanence), evolutionists believe in an evolving completion. *Hoimar von Ditfurth* sees this completion as being "the beyond" [D3 p 300-301]:

> "The assurance given by theologians that the kingdom of God lies 'beyond' this world, seems to refer to a land that cannot find a place for itself. In an evolving world developing towards its completion, something quite different is expected. The fact of evolution has opened our eyes to realise that reality cannot end there where our familiar reality ends. Neither philosophy, nor science theory could compel us to recognise the 'transcendental immanence' which will far surpass our present stage of development – it was evolution that opened our eyes."

The long evolutionary time spans have even infiltrated into evangelical circles. How else is it to be understood when a theologian like *Hansjörg Bräumer* states his position clearly as follows [B6 p 32]: "For anybody who chooses to practise science with God, the basic thought patterns are fixed." Then, a few pages later, he writes [p 44]: "It detracts nothing from the creation account to see it happening in a cyclic framework of millions of years."

Supporters of theistic evolution corrupt the biblically given measures of time. It is noteworthy, but sad, that such authors invariably quote the Irish bishop *J Ussher*, who calculated that the earth was created in the year 4004 B C. To ensure that the reader will really be convinced of the ridiculousness of such a procedure, the clinching comment of his contemporary, *J Lightfoot*, usually follows, namely that it happened at 9 o'clock in the morning of October 23. In this way they attempt to divest themselves completely of the biblical time-scale. *Ussher* was correct in basing his calculations on the biblical genealogies; but he went beyond the actual biblical time-frame when he arrived at an exact date. On the other hand, the evolutionist time-scales for which there are no physical grounds (discussed fully in [S5]), can lead to two delusions:

1. *Not all statements of the Bible are to be taken seriously.* If so, then we deny God the trust on which the relationship between believers and God is based (Hebr 10:35). It is probably not a prerequisite for salvation to believe that God created everything in six days, but when one accepts this pronouncement together with all the others, it leads to a true understanding of Scripture.

2. *The required vigilance in our vision of the second coming of Jesus may be lost.* The Bible warns us against people who ask, directly or indirectly, "Where is this 'coming' he promised?" and who make us believe that "everything goes on as it has since the beginning of creation" (2 Peter 3:4).

8.8 Danger No 8: Misinterpretation of Reality

Certain statements which appear constantly in evolutionist publications, should let us prick up our ears:

– "No serious biologist doubts the fact that evolution has happened, nor that all living creatures are cousins of one another." (*R Dawkins* [D2 p 287]).

- "Never before has a doctrine set up by a single person ... been proved to be so true, as the theory of descent formulated by *Charles Darwin*" *(K Lorenz).*

Why does the doctrine of evolution require such assurances? One will never find such confessions of belief in scientific journals dealing with physics, chemistry, or informatics. On the contrary, authors in these disciplines are inclined to comment reservedly on their results. *Nietzsche's* maxim seems to apply to evolutionary philosophy: "Convictions are worse enemies of truth than lies."

Science-theoretical analysis along the lines of theorems P1 to P10 leads to the conclusion that the "theory of evolution" does not qualify as a scientific theory. Some examples will clarify this statement:

- No natural process which resulted in information forming automatically in matter, has ever been observed. Neither is this possible in the most spectacular or costly experiments (contradiction of theorem P10).

- No transition from one basic kind to another has ever been observed (contradiction of theorem P10).

- The *"hypercycle theory"* devised by *M Eigen* for explaining the origin of the first life, has never been verified experimentally. And this conceptual system also does not qualify to be a theory (compare P7 and P10), neither is there any relation with reality.

- The frequently quoted transitional forms and "missing links" have never been found. All fossils represent complete, perfect organisms.

It has also become clear from the scientific objections discussed above (OB1 to OB20), that evolution cannot "deliver the goods" as pretended by its supporters. The question rightly arises why it is believed so emphatically, while the creation account of the Bible is so readily brushed aside, as is, for example, done by *Dawkins* [D2 p 316]: "The

Genesis story is just the one that happened to have been adopted by one particular tribe of Middle Eastern herders. It has no more special status than the belief of a particular West African tribe that the world was created from excrement of ants." But *Dawkins* himself declares in a clear statement of preconceived belief (page 337): If I am correct, this means that, even if no factual evidence for *Darwin's* theory is available, it is certainly justifiable to accept it above all other rival theories.

If evolution is false, as we have stated many times with the aid of scientific and biblical arguments, then numerous sciences are built on a false foundation. Whenever they conform with evolutionary views, they arrive at a misrepresentation of reality. If the biblical doctrine of creation is true, then we can practise a better science based on the truth. Creation research is therefore mandatory on the following grounds:

- The formulated theories are based on biblical statements; they are believed to be true, "a priori".

- We will be able to practise a far better and more correct science in all those areas where biblical statements provide us with unassailable basic information (e. g. sin, Noah's flood, human nature).

- Results obtained in creation research will be in accordance with the central teachings of the Bible. This feedback provides us with a true understanding of the Bible.

- If we can abundantly demonstrate with scientific results that the Bible establishes itself exactly there where it is at present questioned and disbelieved most, then it becomes clear that its statements on salvation are equally certain.

- Behind and in all works we see the power and wisdom of God (Rom 1:19; Col 2:3).

- Research brings joy: "Great are the works of the Lord; they are pondered by all who delight in them" (Ps 111:2).

8.9 Danger No 9: Loss of Creation Concepts

We must distinguish clearly between research which investigates the creation around us, and contemplation of the beginnings of creation. The present universe can be investigated scientifically by using available research methods (measure, weigh, observe, experiment). These resources are also available for creation research, subject to the stated basic assumptions. But this is essentially impossible for the six days of creation (see basic assumption C6). Knowledgeable engineers can investigate the functions and efficiency of a completed machine, as well as the principles of construction and the materials employed. But most questions about its origin cannot be answered by studying only the machine itself (e. g. country where it was manufactured, who the builder was, or on what concepts the construction was based). Only the original builder himself can provide relevant and sufficient information on these aspects. How much more is this true of all creative works? It is not possible to extrapolate our understanding of present-day natural laws back into creation week, because they were only then set up and "pieced together".

Some essential creation principles are taught in the Bible:

- Anything that was created instantaneously, must have had a certain appearance of age at the time according to present experiences:

  • Adam probably looked like a man of twenty

  • A sunflower would seem to be three months old

  • Eden's tall trees would appear to be 80 years old

- The Andromeda galaxy would be rated to be 2.3 million years old according to its distance.

God does not deceive us with these appearances of age. On the contrary, we ourselves introduce this age tension because of our present-day views.

- God created matter without using any available material. None of our current natural laws can explain this.

- God created the earth first, and on the fourth day He added the moon, the solar system, the local galaxy, and all other star systems. Their origin cannot be explained in terms of current laws of gravity or *Kepler's* laws.

On the other hand, according to evolutionary beliefs it is possible to explain origins by means of natural laws (see basic assumption E4). However, this is not possible in the biblical view. The biblical creation principles are ignored in theistic evolution, but, on the other hand, evolutionary ideas are carried into the Bible. In this way God's omnipotent acts are eventually negated. The apocryphal book of Sirach (Chapter 18:1-7) is of topical interest in our time:

"He Who lives for ever, has created everything without exception. The Lord alone is always right. He has given nobody the ability to describe His works adequately; no-one can research their entire greatness. Who can measure His awesome power? Who can count all proofs of His mercy? No-one can detract anything from them, and nobody can add anything. It is impossible to fathom all His wonders. If someone thinks that he has reached the end of his report, then he discovers that he is still at the very beginning. And when he stops, it is because he does not know how to proceed".

8.10 Danger No 10: Missing the Purpose

On the question of purposes we encounter a very important point of difference between biblical and evolutionary thought. In no other historical book do we find so many and such valuable statements of purpose for man, as in the Bible. As some examples illustrate:

1. *Man is God's purpose with creation:* "So God created man in His own image, in the image of God He created him" (Gen 1:27).

2. *Man is the object of God's love:* "I have loved you with an everlasting love; I have drawn you with loving-kindness" (Jer 31:3).

3. *Man is the purpose of God's plan of redemption:* "But He was pierced for our transgressions, He was crushed for our iniquities. The punishment that brought us peace, was upon Him, and by His wounds we are healed" (Isaiah 53:5).

4. *Man is the purpose of the mission of God's Son:* "This is how God showed His love among us: He sent His one and only Son into the world that might live through Him" (1 John 4:9).

5. *We are the purpose of God's inheritance:* "So that, having been justified by His grace, we might become heirs having the hope of eternal life" (Titus 3:7).

6. *Heaven is our destination:* "But our citizenship is in heaven" (Phil 3:20).

The very thought of purposefulness is anathema to evolutionists. There are no blueprints, nor any purpose (see basic assumption E8): "There are no causes working from the future and thus no previously established purpose of evolution" *(H von Ditfurth)*. Similar views are expressed by *H Penzlin*, a biologist of Eastern Germany [P2 p 19]: "Evolutionary adaptations never follow a purposeful pro-

gramme, they can thus not be regarded as teleonomical."
In a comprehensive overview *Penzlin* discussed the problem confronting evolutionary doctrine of explaining the purposefulness observed in the world of organisms, without recourse to a Creator and Master Builder; the purposefulness itself cannot be denied. What a remarkable and contradictory brashness (compare Romans 1:19-22)! In 1861 *Karl Marx* wrote to *Ferdinand Lasalle* that *Darwin's* work dealt a death blow to teleology [P2 p 9]. *Penzlin* endeavoured to interpret the word "teleological" in biology in such a way that it would not mean anything purposeful. Another proposal from the ranks of evolution supporters is to introduce the word *"teleonomy"* to replace *"teleology"*. *C S Pittendrigh* explains that the former word would not refer to a plan or a purpose in all known cases of purposefulness [P4].

If man is not the explicit end-product of evolution, as evolutionists believe unanimously, then man's existence has no meaning. This aspect was developed abstractly by *Carsten Bresch* [B7 p 21]:

> "Nature seems to be a purposeless and meaningless machine. Did we pay for our new mental freedom by sacrificing the meaning of our existence? Partially knowledgeable man stands alone, uprooted in an icy universe, lost in the chain of generations which arose from nothing, and become nothing. What is the purpose of it all? Is this the desired purpose of understanding, the last great answer to all questions asked of nature? Man has 'experimented' himself out of a Godly order, away from an inner feeling of security … He has made a taboo of the question of the meaning of human life – its portal has been nailed shut with planks. He no more dares to touch it, because he fears to find the dismal answer that our life has no meaning at all."

Sigmund Freud is never attacked as viciously from certain quarters as the founder of the theory of evolution, although *Freud* had consistently taught that belief in a god is really nothing but a form of 'infantile wishful thinking'."
Von Ditfurth is correct when he states that we criticise the teachings ascribed to *Darwin*, but it is wrong to say that we are attacking the person of *Darwin*. Atheism can be recognised immediately, independent of the philosophical attire it appears in, so that it is not directly dangerous for Christians. But the situation is quite different in the case of conceptual structures which appear in sheep's clothing, and subsequently become "ferocious wolves" as described by Jesus (Matt 7:15). In the case of theistic evolution Christian concepts are readily integrated. However, such teachings reduce the message of the Bible to insignificance and come as "savage wolves" who "will not spare the flock" (Acts 20:29). All systems which entice us away from the true gate (Jesus) into the sheep pen, are called thieves and robbers by Jesus (John 10:1). If man is unplanned, then he also has no purpose. But if he does not heed the purpose set out for him, then he will miss it. For this reason the Bible warns repeatedly:

> "We must pay more careful attention, therefore, to what we have heard, so that we do not drift away" (Hebr 2:1).

> "Do not let anyone … disqualify you for the prize (Col 2:18).

> "See to it that no-one takes you captive through hollow and deceptive philosophy, which depends on human tradition and the basic principles of this world rather than on Christ" (Col 2:8).

References

[B1] Beck, H. W.:   Genesis
– Aktuelles Dokument vom
Beginn der Menschheit –
Neuhausen-Stuttgart, 1983

[B2] Benesch, H.:   Der Ursprung des Geistes,
München, 1980

[B3] v. Bertalanffy, L.:   Das biologische Weltbild,
Bern, 1949

[B4] Blechschmidt, E.:   Gestaltungsvorgänge in der
menschlichen Embryonal-
entwicklung
in: W. Gitt (Hrsg.), Am An-
fang war die Information,
Gräfelfing/München, 1982

[B5] Böhme, W.:   Evolution und Freiheit
in: Herrenalber Texte
Nr. HT 57, 1984, S. 88-93

[B6] Bräumer, H.:   Wuppertaler Studienbibel
– Das erste Buch Mose
Kap. 1 bis 11 –
Wuppertal, 1983

[B7] Bresch, C.:   Zwischenstufe Leben –
Evolution ohne Ziel?
Frankfurt/M., 1979

[B8] Breuer, R.:   Vom Ende der Welt
Bild der Wissenschaft (1981),
H. 1, S. 47-55

[D1] Davies, P.:   God and the New Physics
London, 1983

[D2] Dawkins, R.:	The Blind Watchmaker, 1986
[D3] v. Ditfurth, H.:	Wir sind nicht nur von dieser Welt, München, 1984
[E1] Eccles, J. C., Zeier, H.:	Gehirn und Geist München, 1980
[E2] Ellinger, T.:	Schöpfung und Wissenschaft – Denkansätze der Studiengemeinschaft WORT UND WISSEN –, Neuhausen-Stuttgart, 1988
[G1] Gipper, H.:	Sprachursprung und Spracherwerb in: Herrenalber Texte Nr. HT 66, 1985, S. 65-88
[G2] Gitt, W.:	Logos oder Chaos – Aussagen und Einwände zur Evolutionslehre sowie eine tragfähige Alternative – Neuhausen-Stuttgart, 2. überarb. und erw. Aufl. 1985
[G3] Gitt, W.:	Ordnung und Information in Technik und Natur in: W. Gitt (Hrsg.), Am Anfang war die Information, Gräfelfing/München, 1982
[G4] Gitt, W.:	What about the other Religions? Christl. Literaturverbreitung Bielefeld, 1993
[G5] Gitt, W.:	Das biblische Zeugnis der Schöpfung Neuhausen-Stuttgart, 5. Aufl. 1993

[G6] Gitt, W.: So steht's geschrieben
– Zur Wahrhaftigkeit der
Bibel –
Neuhausen-Stuttgart,
3. Aufl. 1993

[G7] Gitt, W.: Energie – optimal durch
Information
Neuhausen-Stuttgart, 1986

[G8] Gitt, W.: Signale aus dem All
Bielefeld, 1993

[G9] Gitt, W.: Information und Entropie
als Bindeglieder diverser
Wissenschaftszweige
PTB-Mitteilungen 91(1981),
S. 1-17

[G10] Gitt, W.: Information: The Third
Fundamental Quantity
Siemens Review, Vo. 56,
No. 6, Nov/Dec 1989, p 2-7

[G11] Gitt, W.: Questions – I have always
wanted to ask
Bielefeld, 1992

[H1] Hansen, K.: Ein Streifzug durch die
Geschichte des Lebens, seine
Entstehung und Entwicklung
Kultur & Technik (1980),
H. 3, S. 25-37

[H2] Hartwig-
Scherer, S.: Ramapithecus – Vorfahr
des Menschen?
Berlin, 1988

[H3] Havemann, R.: Dialektik ohne Dogma
– Naturwissenschaft und
Weltanschauung –
Reinbek, 1964

[H4] Heckmann, O.   Sterne, Kosmos, Weltmodelle
München, 1980

[I1] Illies, J.:   Für eine menschenwürdigere
Zukunft
Freiburg/Br., 5. Aufl. 1977

[I2] Illies, J.:   Biologie und Menschenbild
Freiburg/Br., 2. Aufl. 1977

[I3] Illies, J.:   Schöpfung oder Evolution
Zürich, 1979

[I4] Illies, J.:   Der Jahrhundertirrtum
– Würdigung und Kritik des
Darwinismus –
Frankfurt/M, 1983

[I5] Illies, J.:   Mit dem Kopf durch den
Sand
Deutsches Allgemeines
Sonntagsblatt vom 7.5.1978

[J1] Jantsch, E.:   Die Selbstorganisation des
Universums
München, 1979

[J2] Junker, R.;
Scherer, S.:   Entstehung und Geschichte
der Lebewesen
– Daten und Deutungen für
den schulischen Bereich –
Gießen, 1986

[J3] Junker, R.:   Rudimentäre Organe
Berlin, 1989

[K1] Kaplan, R. W.:   Der Ursprung des Lebens
Stuttgart, 1. Aufl. 1972

[K2] Kübler-Ross, E.:   Reif werden zum Tode
Gütersloh, 3. Aufl. 1983

[K3] Küppers, B.-O.:   Ordnung aus den Chaos
München, 1987

[K4] Küppers, B.-O.:   Der Ursprung biologischer
                         Information
                         – Zur Naturphilosophie der
                         Lebensentstehung –
                         München, Zürich, 1986

[K5] Kuhn, H.:   Selbstorganisation
                         molekularer Systeme und die
                         Evolution des genetischen
                         Apparats
                         Angewandte Chemie
                         84(1972), S. 838-862

[K5] Kuhn, T. S.:   Die Struktur wissenschaft-
                         licher Revolutionen
                         Frankfurt/M., 1973

[L1] Läpple, A.:   Die Bibel - heute,
                         München, 1974

[L2] Lorenz, K.:   Das sogenannte Böse
                         – Zur Naturgeschichte der
                         Aggression –
                         München, 6. Aufl. 1979

[M1] Mayr, E.:   Gedanken zur Evolutions-
                         biologie
                         Naturwissenschaften
                         75(1969), H. 8, S. 392-397

[M2] Mohr, H.:   Leiden und Sterben als
                         Faktoren der Evolution
                         in: Herrenalber Texte
                         Nr. HT 44, 1983, S. 9-25

[M3] Monod, J.:   Chance and Necessity
                         London, 1972

[O1] Oeing-Hanhoff, L.: Das Böse im Weltlauf
                         in: Herrenalber Texte
                         Nr. HT 44, 1983, S. 50-67

[O2] Osche, G.:   Die Motoren der Evolution
– Zweckmäßigkeit als
biologisches Problem –
Biologie in unserer Zeit
1(1971), S. 51-61

[P1] v. Padberg, L.:   Dialog zwischen Christentum
und Weltreligionen
Bibel und Gemeinde 87(1987),
H. 1, S. 37-45

[P2] Penzlin, H.:   Das Teleologie-Problem in
der Biologie
Biologische Rundschau
25(1987), S.7-26

[P3] Peters, D. S.:   Das Biogenetische Grund-
gesetz – Vorgeschichte und
Folgerungen
Medizinhistorisches Journal
(1980), S. 57-69

[P4] Pittendrigh, C. S.:   Adaption, natural selection,
and behavior
In: Behavior and Evolution.
(Roe, A., G. G. Simpson, Eds.).
Yale University Press, New
Haven 1958, p. 390-416

[P5] Popper, K. R.:   The Logic of Scientific
Discovery
London, 1959, 10th Edition

[P6] Popper, K. R.:   Das Elend des Historizismus
Tübingen, 5. Aufl. 1979

[R1] Rensch, B.:   Das universale Weltbild
– Evolution und Natur-
philosophie –
Frankfurt/M., 1977

[R2] Riedl, R.:	Die Strategie der Genesis München, Zürich, 3. Aufl. 1984
[S1] Sachsse, H.:	Der Begriff der Evolution in der Sicht der Naturwissenschaft und der Philosophie in: Herrenalber Texte Nr. HT 52, 1983, S. 42-59
[S2] Scherer, S., Lambert, G.:	Korrekturlesemechanismen beim biologischen Informationstransfer Naturwissenschaftliche Rundschau 39(1986), S. 20-23
[S3] Scheven, J.:	Karbonstudien – Neues Licht auf das Alter der Erde – Neuhausen-Stuttgart, 1986
[S4] Scheven, J.:	Mega-Sukzessionen und Klimax im Tertiär – Katastrophen zwischen Sintflut und Eiszeit – Neuhausen-Stuttgart, 1988
[S5] Schneider, H.:	Der Urknall und die absoluten Datierungen Neuhausen-Stuttgart, 1982
[S6] Siewing, R. (Hrsg.):	Evolution – Bedingungen – Resultate – Konsequenzen – Stuttgart, New York, 2. bearb. Aufl. 1982
[S7] Stegmüller, W.:	Metaphysik, Skepsis, Wissenschaft Berlin, Heidelberg, New York, 2. Aufl. 1969

[T1] Tanner, W.:   Altern und Tod aus der Sicht
           der Biologie
           Biologie in unserer Zeit,
           10(1980), S. 45-51

[W1] v. Wahlert, G.u.H.: Was Darwin noch nicht
           wissen konnte
           München, 1981

[W2] Weinberg, S.:   The First Three Minutes
           – A Modern View of the
           Origin of the Universe –
           London, 1977

[W3] v. Weizsäcker, C. F.: Evolution und
           Entropiewachstum
           Festvortrag anl. der Jahres-
           tagung der Deutschen
           Ges. für Biophysik,
           Regensburg 1976, Sonder-
           druck der Stadt Regensburg.

[W4] Wieland, W.:   Möglichkeiten und Grenzen
           der Wissenschaftstheorie
           Angewandte Chemie
           93(1981), S. 627-634

[W5] Wuketits, F. M.: Biologie und Kausalität
           Berlin, Hamburg, 1981, 165 S.

[W6] Wuketits, F. M.: Evolutionäre Erkenntnis-
           theorie als neue Synthese
           in: Herrenalber Texte
           Nr. HT 52, 1983, S. 29-41

[W7] Wuketits, F. M.: Gesetz und Freiheit in der
           Evolution
           Umschau 79(1979), S. 268-275

Index of Authors

Altner, G.	92
Beck, H. W.	8, 50, 89
Benesch, H.	48, 49
Bertalanffy, L. v.	37
Blechschmidt, E.	47
Böhme, W.	93
Bohr, N.	77
Bräumer, H.-J.	101
Bresch, C.	16, 17, 67, 108
Breuer, R.	53, 54, 57, 87
Chardin, T. de	58, 92, 93
Darwin, Ch.	46, 49, 77, 103, 104, 108, 109
Davies, P.	53, 82
Dawkins, R.	102, 103, 104
Ditfurth, H. v.	13, 16, 91, 92, 94, 96, 101, 107
Dyson, F.	57
Eccles, J.	50
Eigen, M.	38, 76, 103
Einstein, A.	14
Engels, F.	48, 76
Fischer, E. H.	76
Freud, S.	49, 109
Fromm, E.	49
Gardner	31
Gipper, H.	30, 31, 32
Haeckel, E.	46, 47, 76, 99

Hansen, K.	62
Havemann, R.	34
Heckmann, O.	16, 53
Hegel, G. W. F.	40
Hubble, E. P.	13, 53
Humboldt, W. v.	31
Illies, J.	24, 30, 32, 51, 88, 92, 95, 98
Jantsch, E.	77, 98
Jonas, H.	99
Junker, R.	8, 64
Kahane, E.	13
Kaminski, J.	8
Kant, I.	40
Kaplan, R. W.	33, 34, 37
Keith, A.	17
Kepler, J.	106
Kies, J.	8
Kübler-Ross, E.	38
Küppers, B.-O.	16, 71, 73, 76, 83, 84
Kuhn, H.	76, 77
Kuhn, T. S.	82
Läpple, A.	24
Lasalle, F.	108
Lessing, G. E.	40
Lightfoot, J.	102
Lorenz, K.	15, 30, 49, 88, 103
Marquardt, B.	31
Marx, K.	108
Mayr, E.	77

McKay, D. M.	74
Mohr, H.	15, 36, 38, 51, 52, 95
Monod, J.	27, 59, 72
Nee, W.	50
Neidhardt, J.	50
Nietzsche, F.	59, 103
Oeing-Hanhoff, L.	21
Osche, G.	62, 64
Padberg, L. v.	44
Pauli, W.	25
Pasteur, L.	22
Penzlin, H.	107, 108
Peters, D. S.	46, 63
Pittendrigh, C. S.	108
Popper, K. R.	9, 10, 11, 12, 25, 26
Pot, P.	51
Premark	31
Rensch, B.	14, 15, 16, 29, 33, 34, 46
Riedl, R.	27
Rohrbach, H.	92
Ryle, G.	81
Sachsse, H.	93
Scherer, S.	65
Siewing, R.	13, 63, 87
Skinner, C. B.	49
Stegmüller, W.	9
Süssmilch, J. P.	32
Tanner, W.	36, 38
Ussher, J.	102

Wahlert, G. u. W.   76
Watson, J. B.   49
Weinberg, S.   54, 88
Weizsäcker, C. F. v.   36, 92, 93
Westermann, C.   92
Wiener, N.   84
Wuketits, F. M.   13, 48, 55, 59, 87
Zeier, H.   48

Abbreviations of the Books of the Bible

Books of the Old Testament (OT)

Genesis	Gen	Ecclesiastes	Eccl
Exodus	Ex	Song of Solomon	Song
Leviticus	Lev	Isaiah	Isaiah
Numbers	Num	Jeremiah	Jer
Deuteronomy	Deut	Lamentations	Lam
Joshua	Josh	Ezekiel	Ezek
Judges	Judg	Daniel	Dan
Ruth	Ruth	Hosea	Hosea
1 Samuel	1 Sam	Joel	Joel
2 Samuel	2 Sam	AMos	Amos
1 Kings	1 Kings	Obadiah	Obad
2 Kings	2 Kings	Jonah	Jonah
1 Chronicles	1 Chron	Micah	Micah
2 Chronicles	2 Chron	Nahum	Nahum
Ezra	Ezra	Habakkuk	Hab
Nehemiah	Neh	Zephaniah	Zeph
Esther	Esther	Haggai	Hag
Job	Job	Zechariah	Zech
Psalms	Ps	Malachi	Mal
Proverbs	Prov		

Books of the New Testament (NT)

Matthew	Matt	1 Timothy	1 Tim
Mark	Mark	2 Timothy	2 Tim
Luke	Luke	Titus	Titus
John	John	Philemon	Philem
The Acts	Acts	Hebrews	Hebr
Romans	Rom	James	James
1 Corinthians	1 Cor	1 Peter	1 Peter
2 Corinthians	2 Cor	2 Peter	2 Peter
Galatians	Gal	1 John	1 John
Ephesians	Eph	2 John	2 John
Philippians	Phil	3 John	3 John
Colossians	Col	Jude	Jude
1 Thessalonians	1 Thess	Revelation	Rev
2 Thessalonians	2 Thess		

Glossary: Explanation of Terms

We now explain the most important terms used in this book. An arrow → indicates a keyword which is explained elsewhere. In most cases the origin as well as the original meaning of a term is mentioned.

Ad absurdum (Latin *ad* = to, *absurdus* = absurd; non-sensical): When an idea is pursued "ad absurdum", one demonstrates the non-sense of an idea; you show s.o. the absurdity of his statement.

Agnosticism (Greek *agnosía* = no knowledge): The doctrine that reality is unknowable. In particular no knowledge of God is obtainable.

Allegoric (Greek *allegoria* = to say differently): Abstract ideas are represented in a personified way, with symbolic and didactical meanings. Examples: Death is represented as a man with a scythe; justice as a blindfolded woman with scales (Justitia).

Allomones (Greek *allo* = foreign and → hormones): Chemicals that serve as signals between individuals of different kinds. By this means different kinds of animals can coexist peacefully (symbiosis). Example: Blue butterflies (allotinus unicolor) and certain ants (anoplolepis longipes) accept one another. The ants "domesticate" aphids which secrete a sweet liquid when they are "milked" by stroking. The butterflies imitate this stroking movement and also obtain sugar. The caterpillars of these butterflies even consume and destroy some of the aphids, but the ants do not attack them. The reason for this extraordinary tolerance is the allomones which chemically suppress the aggressiveness of the ants (→ hormones, → pheromones).

Amino acids ("amin" is derived from *ammonia* + suffix *in*): Amino acids are the molecular building blocks of → proteins. All amino acids comprise at least a carboxy group (COOH), an amino group (NH_2), and a unique specific radical R. Neutral amino acids have the same number of amino and carboxy groups (e g alanine). In acidic ones R contains a supplementary carboxy group (e g asparagine), and basic ones have an extra amino group in R (e g glutamine). The nomenclature is incidental, but the names usually end with "-ine". Abbreviated three-letter symbols are used internationally:

Alanine   (Ala): $H_3C\text{-}CH(NH_2)\text{-}COOH$

Asparagine (Asp): $HOOC\text{-}CH_2\text{-}CH\text{-}(NH_2)\text{-}COOH$

Glutamine (Gln): $H_2N\text{-}CO\text{-}CH_2\text{-}CH(NH_2)\text{-}COOH$

With the exception of glycine all amino acids possess one or more asymmetrical carbon atoms. All of them, except glycine, are therefore also optically active. This means that they are either left-handed or right-handed. L and D structures can not be superimposed, even when rotated through 180°.

It should be emphasised that only twenty out of a large number of chemically possible amino acids are present in the proteins of all living organisms. It is also noteworthy that all twenty of these amino acids are of the L form. This is difficult to explain in terms of evolution. The sequence of the amino acids in the protein chains determines their secondary and tertiary structures and whether they function as → enzymes or → hormones.

Analogy (Greek *analogos* = similar, accordingly):

1. *General:* When it is difficult or impossible to explain a concept, one compares it with something that is well-known. Example: Jesus used parables to explain the

unknown Kingdom of Heaven in terms of everyday events.

2. *In biology:* Similarities in the functions of organs of different life forms: When organs and structures of different organisms perform the same function, they are called → homologies or analogies in evolutionary terms. Evolutionists often infer that different organisms have common ancestors when they exhibit similar structures; such similarities are called homologies. On the other hand analogies are not regarded as indicative of a common descent. An example of the latter is the gills of fishes and the lungs of mammals. Their structures are quite different, but they perform the same function, namely to absorb oxygen, so that common descent is not assumed in this case. Other examples of analogies are the digging claws of moles and of mole cricket (*gryllotalpidae*), and the wings of birds and insects.

Anthropology (Greek *ánthropos* = man): A subdivision of biology specially concerned with human beings. → Phylogenesis, → ontogenesis, and the geographical variability of human races are studied.

Apobetics (purposefulness; the deductive aspects of information; Greek *apóbainon* = conclusion, result): The highest of the five levels of information (→ statistical, → syntactic, → semantic, → pragmatic, apobetic). It entails the purposefulness of information. The present author introduced this term in 1981, because it implies that the sender provides the purpose, the plan, or the design in order to obtain certain effects in the recipient. This is the highest and most important aspect of information, because it deals with the purpose of the sender. In every case where information is transmitted, the question should be: "Why

127

does the sender transmit this information, and what effects does he want to achieve in the recipient?"

A priori (Latin for pre-established; from before): Refers to assumptions, concepts, or postulates that are not based on experience or observation. They have been logically contrived, or established without proof. On the other hand, "a posteriori" means that a conclusion has been reached after an orderly sequence of chronological, logical, or abstract steps.

Axiom (Greek *axíoma* = fundamental theorem): A postulate which is stated peremptorily and is supposed to be clarifying and undeniable, although it cannot be proved. Any proof relies on one or more unprovable axioms. A mathematical example: If two values are equal to a third one, then they are also equal (i e if $a = x$ and $b = x$, then $a = b$).

Behaviourism: This is a psychological school of thought. In its original form only objective, measurable behaviour is recognised. Concepts like consciousness, soul, and emotions are ignored. All types of behaviour, including speech and thought, are regarded as a question of stimulus and response.

Biochemistry: The science dealing with chemical changes in living organisms (e g metabolism, respiration, digestion). The following problems have thus far been resolved: The structure of proteins, the most important metabolic reactions, the structure and functioning of vitamins and hormones, and the biochemical aspects of heredity.

Biogene (Greek *bíos* = life; *-genes* = causing): Derived from or produced by living substances.

Biogenetics, basic law (the theory of recapitulation): This theory was elevated to a law by *E Haeckel* (1866). According to this view the development of an organism briefly recapitulates (repeats) the genetic history of the species. This idea was already formulated before *Haeckel*s time: In 1821 *Meckel* referred to the similarity between the development of an embryo and of an animal type. In 1828 *K E von Baer* expressed a similar view, as did *F Müller* in 1864. It was assumed that the gill slits of fishes appear during the development of the embryos of the higher vertebrates and of human beings, thus partially repeating their → phylogenesis. This was regarded as a strong argument in favour of evolution. Research has disproved this view, but it is still propagated by evolutionists as a basic principle.

Biotope (Greek *bíos* = life, *topos* = place, position): The typical ecological niche of colonies of animals or plants or even of single kinds, delineated by circumstances like temperature, or soil properties.

Catalyst (Greek *katálysis* = solution): A substance which enables, accelerates or retards a chemical reaction. It is usually required in small quantities only, and because it does not participate in the reaction, it is not changed. Most technical chemical procedures rely on catalysis, as well as those within living cells. Example: Cells produce → enzymes which are → proteins and which greatly accelerate slow chemical reactions.

Chromosome (Greek *chroma* = colour, *soma* = bodies; i e particles made visible by means of colouring): Chromosomes are wiry organelles found in the nucleus of all cells. All body cells have twice as many chromosomes as the reproductive cells. The latter are → haploid (single), whereas body cells are → diploid (double). Chromosomes are never formed anew, but result from the replication (doubling) and complementary division of the available chromosomes.

The number of chromosomes per body cell:

Human	46
Large ape	48
Goldfish	94
Dog	78
Hedgehog	48
Dragon fly (Aeschna)	26
Baboon	42
Marine crab	168
Sheep	54
Beech	84
Ash	46
Oats	42
Mountain algae	ca 1200
Maize	20
Radish	18
Snowdrop	24

It is clear that there is practically no connection between the number of chromosomes and the complexity of an organism. The reason is that chromosomes can be either long or short, and can therefore carry more genes or less.

Code: In informatics a code is defined as a correspondence (mapping) between one set of symbols and another. In general a code is the allocation of one kind of symbols to another kind, or to some aspect of reality, like physics, chemistry, or common events. This correspondence is based on a unique, voluntary prescription or convention. All code sequences are derived from an intellectual process, and can therefore not be ascribed to material causes. All codes represent something else (→ information). For example, the triplet GCA represents alanine, but it does not cause alanine to be formed. All coding sequences are based on a certain plan. For this reason one may decide, purely at the coding level, whether any given system derives from a creative intellectual activity, or whether it has a material cause.

Complementary (Latin *complementum* = increased completion, supplement): Mutually complete. Complementary angles add up to 90°; superimposed complementary colours result in white e g yellow and blue; red and green).

Cosmology (Greek *kosmos* = order, beauty, universe): It is a branch of astronomy which considers theories about the structure of the universe. The distribution of matter in space and their relative motions are investigated. Using known physical theories and local astronomical data, it is endeavoured to devise a complete theory about the properties of the entire universe. This has not yet been indisputably successful.

Cybernetics (Greek *kybernetike, téchne* = the art of steering): *Norbert Wiener* (1894-1964), an American mathematician, employed this term to describe scientific researches dealing with the automatic controlling and steering mechanisms of various (biological, technical, or sociological) systems. Widely diverse fields of research have thus been combined. Technical theories which were originally developed in the study of communications and the flow of information between the different elements of a system, are employed to better understand and explain non-technical phenomena.

Deism (Latin *Deus* = God): The belief in a personal supernatural God who created this world and all its (physical) laws, but who has no influence on world events, on history, or on individuals. This unbiblical idea originated during the "Enlightenment" of the 17th and 18th centuries. Adherents consequently believe that God could not have revealed Himself. This contrasts strongly with biblical doctrine.

Deism originated in Britain during the 17th century as the "religion of reason" (*Cherbury, Toland, Collins, Tindal* and *Hume*); it soon flowed over to France *(Voltaire)*, and reached Germany in the middle of the 18th century *(Lessing, Mendelssohn)*.

Determinism (Latin *determinare* = pre-established, delineated): The doctrine that all events have been pre-determined; everything is a question of cause and effect. In the earlier mechanistic view of the universe all physical processes were regarded as computable. All events based on matter and motion were subject to a strict mechanical process of cause and effect. Modern quantum physics has rejected this general assumption and principle.

Dichotomy (Greek *dichotomía* = divide into two parts): Man is regarded as consisting of two parts, body and soul (a → trichotomy comprises a contrary view).

DNA (= deoxyribo-nucleic acid): The nucleic acids are of paramount importance among the various building blocks of living cells. They contain → genetic information, and they have the ability to implement this information in cells. In 1953 *Watson* and *Crick* deciphered the structure of DNA and showed that these molecules are able to effect replication as well as storing and releasing information.

According to the *Watson-Crick* model DNA molecules comprise two strands of poly-nucleotides wound round another in the shape of a double spiral. Connected by hydrogen bridges, the orientation of all pairs of bases is perpendicular to the axis of the right-winding spiral (or helix). The sequence of the bases in one of the two strands of the spiral automatically determines the sequence in the other one, because the "chemical letters" only occur in complementary pairs: adenine with thymine, and guanine with cytosine. For this reason the molecular ratio of adenine to thymine is always 1:1, as is the ratio guanine: cytosine. And the total number of the "letters" A + G is the same as C + T.

Dimensions: The diameter of the DNA molecule is 2 nanometres (2 thousand millionths of a metre, 1 nm = 10^{-9} m), and the distance between the members of one base pair is 0.34 nm. Consecutive pairs are rotationally staggered by 36°, so that one complete revolution comprises 10 pairs and a vertical increase of 3.4 nm.

Mass: Taking one twelfth of the mass of an atom of carbon-12 as the atomic unit of mass (1 u = 1.6605655 · 10^{-24} g), we find the following:

1 carbon-12 atom	12 u
1 atom of oxygen-16	16 u
1 molecule of water	18 u
1 molecule of insulin	5 700 u
1 haemoglobin molecule	65 000 u
1 molecule of styropore	50 000 000 u
1 DNA molecule of a goldfish	$2.4 \cdot 10^{12}$ u
1 DNA molecule of a dog	$3.2 \cdot 10^{12}$ u
1 molecule of human DNA	$3.5 \cdot 10^{12}$ u

The total length of a molecule of human DNA is approximately 2.7 metres, and the average length for each of the 46 chromosomes is nearly 6 cm (270/46 = 5.87 cm).

DNA molecules are extremely thin, the thickness to length ratio being $1:1.35 \cdot 10^9$. If the diameter of a model of a DNA molecule is 1 m, its total length will be 1350 million km – 3840 times the distance from the earth to the moon (which is 384 000 km) or nine times the distance to the sun (1 astronomical unit = 149 597 870 km).

A molecule of DNA consists of millions of atoms which vibrate and swing continuously; some movements even resemble breathing. The frequency of vibration falls in the same range as the electromagnetic spectrum from radio waves to infra-red radiation. When a DNA molecule splits up, it rotates at a speed of about 250 revolutions per second, and ten thousand "letters" can be copied in a second.

Dualism (Latin *duo* = two): "Twoness", polarity, opposites. The idea that the world is governed or guided by two opposing realities or principles (e g light and darkness, good and evil, God and the devil, spirit and matter).

Dualistic interaction theory: → Interaction

Ecological niche: The totality of the interactive relations between an organism and its environment (nutrition, reproduction, and the predator-prey law). In the present ecological niches environmental conditions allow the survival of certain kinds of animals or plants.

Enzyme (Greek *en* = in; *zyme* = yeast): → protein

Escherichia coli (bacteria living in human intestines, named after the discoverer, the German paediatrician, *Theodor Escherich*, 1857-1911): These bacteria have been studied most often, and are therefore the best known. Their size is about one thousand millionth of a cubic millimeter (10^{-9}mm^3), 500 thousand million of them weigh 1 gram, and they are two thousandths of a millimeter long ($2 \cdot 10^{-6}$m).

Each bacterium, being a single cell, contains two million protein molecules of 1850 different kinds. The chromosomes are ring shaped and consist of more than three million base pairs. One bacterium can divide into two in about 45 minutes, and, under favourable conditions, within 20 minutes. Six rotating electrical devices working at 0.2 volts, can propel a bacterium at a speed of 0.2 mm per second, which is 65 times its length. A comparable speed for a human being would be 400 km per hour.

Explicit (Latin *explicitus* = unfold): Expressed clearly; all aspects of a matter are clearly indicated. Opposite: → implicit.

Gene (Greek *génos* = generation, type, descent): Inheritable factor; the smallest material unit which determines heredity; it is located in the chromosomes. Each gene is responsible for the synthesis of a specific protein, and the genes determine the characteristics of the individual. Genes can be replicated; they are arranged in a linear sequence in the chromosomes, and consist of → DNA molecules.

Genetic code: The genetic → code is the sequence in which the 20 amino acids occurring in all living organisms, are arranged in → triplets. A triplet is a word consisting of three letters. The genetic code employs an "alphabet" of four chemical "letters", namely adenine, guanine, cytosine, and thymine.

Genetic information: The information stored in the nucleic acids. They are essential for the operation of all processes in living cells, and are transmitted unaltered to the next generation of cells when cell division takes place. This identical replication of genetic information is the reason for the constancy of the information carried by the genes and the → genomes in all cells, and for the constancy of heredity. Genetic information plays a centrally important role during the development and growth of individual organisms (→ ontogenesis).

Genome (Greek *génos* = generation, type, heredity): The single (→ haploid) set of chromosomes of a cell and the genes they contain.

Geophysics (Greek *geo* = earth): The science dealing with natural physical phenomena on and inside the earth. Effects deriving from space, especially from the sun and the moon, are also studied. Geophysics include meteorology (study of the atmosphere), hydrology and oceanography (study of water and the oceans), as well as actual earth studies, like the gravitational field of the earth, the earths magnetic field, and the internal structure of the earth.

Haploid (Greek *haploeides* = simple): Refers to cells or organisms having only a single set of chromosomes. Examples: sporozoa (single celled organisms which propagate by means of spores) and some plants, but also the reproductive cells of mammals. The opposite is diploid = two sets of chromosomes. The body (corporeal) cells of mammals and plants are examples of diploid organisms.

Hiatus (Latin *hiatus* = chasm, gap)

Hominid (Latin *homo* = human being): "Human-like", representing existing or extinct human races.

Homology (Greek *homología* = similarity): Similar structures of living organisms (→ analogy). Used in biology as a criterion for investigating and comparing organs and parts of organs according to their structure. In the evolutionary view homologous organs appearing in different organisms indicate that they were derived by descent from one single organ. It is for instance believed that the wings of birds, the anterior fins of fishes, the front legs of mammals, and human arms all stem from a single common primeval organ.

Hormone (Greek *horman* = drive, cause to move): Chemical substance secreted internally into the bloodstream by a gland. They are essential for the proper functioning and coordination of biochemical and physiological processes. The required quantity is of the order of a millionth of a gram. Both the nervous system and the hormones are responsible for the harmonious functioning of all the cells and organs in the human body and in animals. Hormones are carried in the bloodstream to all parts of the body, but they only affect specific organs. This depends on certain properties of the receptors. The quantity of hormones circulating in the blood must always be at the correct level to ensure proper health. Approximately 30 substances, some of which have complex chemical structures, are required continually or periodically for controlling nearly all physiological processes, in humans as well as in all vertebrate animals.

Hypercycle (Greek *hyper* = above): *Manfred Eigen*, a German evolutionist, proposed the idea of a hypercycle, a molecular complex comprising at least two → RNA molecules and two → enzymes. It can supposedly act as a → catalyst for the replication of molecules (the making of identical copies). The hypercycle is regarded as a feedback loop by means of which RNA molecules and enzymes mutually encode one another, resulting in replication. Hypercycles have however not yet been detected experimentally.

Implicit (Latin *implicitus* = complicated): Included. Opposite: → explicit.

Informatics: The name of this young science is a combination of information and technics. It deals with information processing, including computer applications, and the study of non-technical information systems like linguistics and neuron networks.

Information (Latin *informatio* = education, training): Next to matter and energy, information is the third fundamental entity on which both technical and biological processes are based. Information has many facets, and it is often misunderstood. Contradictory statements are made by many authors, and incorrect conclusions are frequently drawn, simply because they refer to information without regard to the proper level (→ statistical, → syntactic, → semantic, → pragmatic or → apobetic). One can for instance not answer the question about the origin of biological systems, if you restrict yourself to the statistical level: The impressive array of mathematical formulas proposed by *Shannon*, does not really explain much. One can only draw well-founded conclusions when the sender-recipient problem is considered at all levels. It is therefore necessary to define the domain of validity of information concepts precisely. The following three principles are important:

1. *The five-levels-principle:* A complete description of the concept of information includes the five aspects: statistics, syntax, semantics, pragmatics, and apobetics. And all these aspects are vital for both the originator and the recipient (see Fig. 2).

2. *The code principle:* Information is established (= formulated, transmitted, or stored) by means of a unique code. An agreed-upon set of symbols is used (e g the alphabet) to form words (→ code). The words have conventional meanings, and they are combined into sentences according to established grammatical rules

(syntax) for the purpose of conveying semantic (mea-ningful) information.

3. *The representation principle:* According to our definition the representative function is a very important charac-teristic of information. Information can never be the thing itself. The encoded symbols only represent the object or the event. The sequences of letters in a news-paper represent the previous days events. History is described in words long after the actual events, and the politicians who are mentioned, are no longer with us. The → triplets in → DNA molecules represent cer-tain amino acids, but the acids themselves are not pre-sent. They will only be formed later according to the encoded information.

To avoid misunderstanding, it should be emphasised that the process of acquiring information through observation, falls outside the scope of our definition. When a painting is contemplated, when a star is observed through a teles-cope, or when the structure of a crystal is studied by me-ans of a microscope, one obtains information by direct ob-servation. The real world itself is studied, and there is thus no question of an encoded representation. Our defi-nition only covers coded representations of events or ob-jects which are not themselves present, or abstract ideas; which are transmitted through space and/or time. The re-presentation principle only holds for encoded correspon-dences or mappings. In all such cases there must always have been a person who established this free allocation of codes to some aspect of reality. In this sense information always requires an intellectual originator.

The theorems mentioned in Chapter 6.1 above, have been derived from experience, like all natural laws. They must verify themselves in the real world around us. If no cont-radictory experiment or example is found, then they beco-me natural laws. Natural laws are significant in that they can be applied to unknown cases. The first moon landing was possible because various natural laws were employed when the voyage was planned and computed. Calculation of the required energy was based on the known laws of energy. Although this law had never before been used for a flight to the moon, its validity was accepted. And it turned out that this trust was justified.

The laws of informatics as expounded here, can be regarded similarly. Once they have been established and justified, they can be applied generally, even to unknown cases. They have been publicly proved, because these information theorems have been justified uncountable times in practice and have not been contradicted experimentally in any laboratory anywhere in the world. The information contained in the cells of all living beings falls inside the domain of the above definition, and the theorems can consequently be applied directly. It follows that such information necessarily requires an intellectual originator. Who this source is, cannot be established within the framework of these theorems, since we have reached the boundary of scientific endeavour.

Figure 2: *The essence of information: Any piece of coded information must have originated in a person (the sender) and is meant for somebody (the recipients). Five inherent levels can be distinguished. On the highest plane, the apobetic level, the purpose and the result of information are found. The second level entails the expected action as well as the resultant activity (pragmatics). The expressed idea and the understood meaning (semantics) occur at the next lower level. And at the fourth level the syntax involves the codification and decoding of the thoughts. The technical and statistical aspects of the actual transmission are found at the lowest level. All five levels clearly and specifically involve both the sender and the recipients, and every single level is a prerequisite for every other one. If a failure occurs at any level, the intended purpose cannot be attained.*

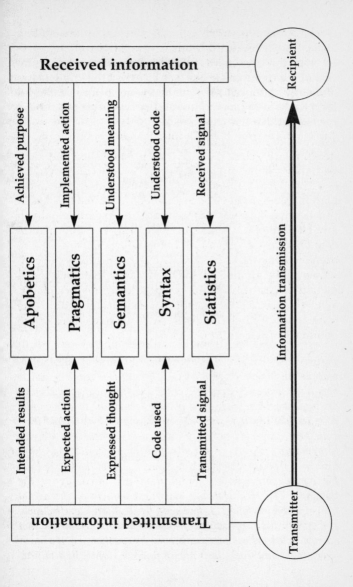

141

Interaction (the theory of *Eccles*; the Latin prefix *inter* means "between" in this case): The actions of persons or components which mutually influence one another. Speech is the most important form of human interaction. According to the interaction theory proposed by John Eccles, a Nobel prize winner, there is a mutual interactive relation between mans brain and his spirit. This means that information is being interchanged between the two. Eccles makes a clear distinction between the brain as a physical component, and the unique non-material spirit. In this way he established that human beings have a non-material part, contradictory to materialistic philosophies.

Language: All systems of expression (language calculus) which can carry meanings (intellectual substrates, thoughts, non-material contents of consciousness), are known as languages. Information can only be transmitted and stored by means of language. The information itself is completely independent of the actual transmission system employed (acoustic, optical, or electrical), and it also does not depend on the method of storage (brain, book, compact disk, electronic data processing system, or magnetic tape). This invariance of information is the result of its being non-material.

Different kinds of languages can be distinguished:

1. Natural languages used for interpersonal communication.

2. Artificial languages (e g Esperanto), sign languages like that used by deaf persons, flag codes, and traffic signs.

3. Formal artificial languages: logical and mathematical calculus, chemical symbols, musical notation, algorithmic language, programming languages like Ada, ALGOL, BASIC, C, C++, COBOL, FORTRAN, Pascal, PL/1.

4. Special technical languages: Building and construction plans, circuit diagrams, and switching diagrams used in electronic design, hydraulics, and pneumatics.

5. Special languages employed by living organisms: → Genetic codes, bee dances, → pheromones used by various insects, hormonal language, web signals of spiders, language used by dolphins, instincts (e g the migratory flight of birds, the migrations of salmon and of eels). The latter should rather be referred to as communication systems.

All languages employ defined sets of characters where the single symbols or the elements of speech are provided with fixed, conventional rules and meaning allocations. All languages contain units or forms (like morphemes, lexemes, expressions, and even entire sentences) which serve as conveyors of meaning. Meanings are internal lingual allocations agreed upon by both sender and recipient. The following resources are involved in the meaningful codification of human languages: Morphology, syntax (grammar, style), phonetics, intonation, and gesticulations, as well as numerous semantic resources (e g homonyms, homophones, metaphors, synonyms, antonyms, paraphrasing, anomalies, and irony).

All communications between senders and recipients entail the formulation of the symbols (sememes; Greek *sema* = symbol) by means of a certain language and their subsequent comprehension. During the formulation stage the information to be transmitted is generated by the thoughts of the sender according to a suitable system (language). And in the comprehension process the recipient analyses the set of symbols and converts them into the corresponding ideas. In accordance with the most general notions, we mean by senders and recipients either intelligent beings, or systems designed by intelligent beings.

Macro molecule (Greek *makro* = long or large): A molecule comprising a large number of components arranged in chains or as interlinked networks. Very many natural and artificial molecules are macro molecules (e g cellulose, → proteins, → DNA, polyethylene, and nylon). Biological macro molecules mostly occur in the form of linear chains (DNA, proteins).

Marginal (Latin *margo* = edge): Situated at the edge. It often refers to notes along the edges of a document or a book.

Meiosis (Greek *meiotis* = decrease in size): Meiotic division, division when ripe, or a reduction; this process of cell division takes place in two stages when germ cells become "ripe" during sexual reproduction. Two consecutive nuclear divisions result in the reduction of the set of → diploid chromosomes.

Microbiology (Greek *mikrós* = small): The biology of micro-organisms, comprising bacteriology (study of bacteria), mycology (fungi), phycology (algae), protozoology (unicellular protozoa), and virology (virusses).

Molecular Darwinism: *Manfred Eigen, Berd-Olaf Küppers,* and other evolutionists assume that Darwinistic evolution must take place at the molecular level. Their purpose is to describe the origin of life as an exclusively physical-chemical process occurring amongst molecules. In this way life is erroneously regarded as a purely materialistic phenomenon.

Monon: This term has been proposed by *Carsten Bresch*, a German geneticist who supports the doctrine of evolution. He regards evolution as a succession of increasingly more complex samples or models. Eventually all forms of life on earth will be united in a gigantic "intellectual organism" – the "monon". This is supposed to be the final result of the all-inclusive integration of the evolution of a planet. The monon is a gigantic historically developing monster consisting of biologically organised matter, and which comprises a supra-individual totality.

Mpc (mega parallax second = megaparsec): 1 Mpc = 10^6 pc. As a light year, a parsec (parallax second) is an astronomical unit of distance. It is the distance at which 1 AU (astronomical unit = the distance from the earth to the sun = 149 597 870 km) subtends an angle of one second (1" = 1/3600 degree). So 1 pc = 1 AU/tan(1") = $30.857 \cdot 10^{12}$ km. It follows that 1 pc = 206 265 AU = 30 857 thousand million km = 3.2617 light years.

Mytosis (Greek *mitos* = strand or string): Mytotic division, indirect nuclear division, equal division; the process of cell nucleus division where two daughter nuclei are formed from one. They contain exactly the same genetic material as the "mother" nucleus, as well as the same number of chromosomes, while the process of → meiosis results in half as many. Body cells divide mytotically, but reproductive cells divide by means of meiosis.

Niche adaptation: Of a supposedly evolving system in an → ecological niche.

Ontogenesis (Greek *óntos* = living being, *génesis* = birth, origin, creation): The growth and development of an organism from conception until it is a sexually mature individual. Ontogenesis is a purposeful process controlled programmatically by the inherent genetic information and the pre-ordained organic totality. In contrast, such guiding information is completely lacking in → phylogenesis.

Peptide (Greek *peptós* = cooked, digested) : → Protein

Perpetuum mobile (Latin, automatic continuous motion): An imaginary machine that can run and work continuously without any input of energy. Since the law of conservation of energy has been generally accepted as a natural law, it is realised that such a machine is impossible.

Pheromone (a combination of Greek *phérein* = carry, and → hormone): A substance secreted by animals that elicits a certain reaction in other animals of the same kind. This term was first used by *Karlson* and *Lüscher* in 1959 for these chemical "messengers" released to the environment. (Perfumes used by women and men may be regarded as artificial pheromones.)

Phylogenesis (Greek *phylon* = tribe, generation; *génesis* = origin): The supposed evolutionary development of living organisms from single cells to human beings. Compare → ontogenesis.

Pit organ: Some snakes possess special organs which can detect heat at a distance. The rattlesnake *(Crotalus spec.)* has two such organs located between its eyes and nostrils on both sides of its head. Their diameter is approximately 3 mm and they are covered with nerve-rich membranes which are 15 micrometers (= 0.015 mm) thick. This pair of heat sensitive organs resemble concave mirrors, so that the direction of a heat source can be ascertained accurately. They are so sensitive that differences of a few thousandths of a degree can be detected. Together with the direction-finding capacity, this enables snakes to locate their prey in the dark.

Pleistocene (Greek *pleistos* = most, + kainós = new, recent): A supposed evolutionary-geological era in the history of the earth. It is a subdivision of the Quaternary era, and precedes the Holocene; it includes the ice ages. The Pleistocene era supposedly lasted from 2 million years ago to ten thousand years ago.

Pragmatics (the behavioural aspect of information: Greek *pragmatiké, téchne* = the art of doing the correct thing): The fourth of the five information levels (→ statistical, → syntactic, → semantic, pragmatic, → apobetic). The question of the purpose of the sender does not arise in the three lower levels. Through every act of transmitting information, the sender intends to affect the behaviour of the recipient in a certain way. To obtain the desired effect, the sender has to consider the way in which the recipient could be compelled to act according to the planned purpose. The concept "pragmatics" expresses this aspect of behaviour. In everyday life it is insufficient to simply string some sentences together, no, we formulate requests, complaints, questions, prompts, threats, commands, appeals, etc to try to elicit the required behaviour. *W Strombach* defined information as a structure which causes something to happen in the receiving system, thus emphasising this important aspect of behaviour. The actions of the recipient are based on information that has previously been assembled by the sender with a specific purpose in mind.

Protein (Greek *protos* = primeval matter): Proteins comprise one of the large groups of macro-molecular substances. Just as cellulose provides the structural elements in plants, so proteins perform a similar function in animals and human beings. Not only does each kind of animal or each human race have distinctive proteins, but each individual person or animal has unique proteins which are recognised as foreign material by others of the same kind and are consequently rejected (immune reaction). Many special proteins having distinctive functions, occur in all living organisms (plants, animals, and human beings); they are known as → enzymes. Enzymes are → catalysts which control and steer growth and metabolic processes, as well as all the reactions involved.

Proteins are → macro-molecules formed by the concatenation (joining of chains) of → amino acid residues. Two amino acids form a dipeptide, three form a tripeptide, etc, and many of them comprise a polypeptide. Some compounds consisting of relatively few building blocks, are known as oligopeptides, but when there are 50 or more components, they are called proteins. Most of the proteins occurring in living organisms consist of hundreds and even thousands of amino acid building blocks. The kind of protein depends on the specific sequence of the amino acids in the chain, as well as the length of the chain. When a chain has a length of 100, the 20 different amino acids occurring in living beings, can be arranged in $20^{100} = 10^{130}$ different sequences. This means that the total number of different proteins that can possibly be formed, exceeds the estimated number of atoms in the universe. The human body alone contains more than 50 000 different proteins.

Protoplasm: This is the living substance of which all human, animal, and plant cells are made. All metabolic processes take place in the protoplasm.

Recombination: In the process of sexual reproduction, genes of the two parents are arranged in new combinations, so that a different mix of the individual characteristics of the parents appear in each offspring.

RNA (= ribo-nucleic acid): A macro-molecule that is similar to → DNA, but consists of one strand only. It is however known that some virusses contain two-strand RNA which has a double helix structure similar to the *Watson-*

Crick model for DNA. Various different RNA molecules which perform certain tasks in cellular metabolism, exist.

Semantics (the meaningfulness of information; Greek *semantikós* = significant, characteristic): The third of the five conceptual levels of information (→ statistical, → syntactic, semantic, → pragmatic, → apobetic). Grammatical rules of syntax together with strings of symbols are required to establish information. The most important aspect of transmitted information is however not the selected code, nor the size, number, or shape of the symbols (letters). Neither is it the method of transmission (writing; or optical, acoustic, electrical, tactile, or olfactory signals). No, the actual meaning of the message (the semantic aspect) is of vital importance (semantic). This central aspect of information, its meaning, does however not play any role in the storage and transmission of the information. The cost of a telegram does not depend on the gravity of the message, but purely on the number of words used. However, the central issue for both the sender and the recipient is the meaning of the conveyed message; it is this meaning that turns the set of symbols into information.

A significant aspect of any piece of information is that it originates with somebody and is intended for somebody. Both a sender and a recipient are always involved in all cases of information transfer. We can thus conclude that information must always have a meaning (semantic level). And because meaning is an intellectual concept, we may further conclude that all information must have an intellectual or spiritual source (sender).

Singularity (Latin *singularitas* = being unique or alone): The peculiarity or uniqueness of an event or of a process. Used in mathematics for a certain point on a curve or on a plane where a situation occurs which differs from the normal behaviour of that curve or plane.

Statistics: The lowest of the five conceptual levels of information (statistics, → syntax, → semantic, → pragmatic, → apobetic). The statistical aspect of information allows us to describe quantitatively those properties of languages that are based on frequency of use. It is of no concern whether a string of symbols conveys any meaning or not. The question of grammatical correctness is also completely excluded at this level. When a set of symbols is essentially a statistical sequence, i e when it is the result of a statistical process, or a purely physical or chemical process, it cannot be regarded as information in terms of our definition.

Subgenual organs: Many insects (e g cockroaches and locusts) possess very sensitive organs for detecting vibrations of the surface on which they stand. This organ (= the subgenual organ), consisting of complex sensory cells, is located in the legs; it can detect extremely small vibrations of the surface.

Syntax (the theory of the structure of sentences; Greek *syntaxis* = arrangement): This is the second of the five conceptual levels of information (→ statistical, syntax, → semantic, → pragmatic, → apobetic). Every language has very definite rules which underlie the grouping of symbols into words and sentences. These rules are based on established conventions. On the syntax level a set of symbols is required for conveying information. Most written languages employ letters, but for other purposes very many diverse conventions are in use: Morse code, hieroglyphs, international flag codes, musical notes, various electronic codes, genetic codes, different stances and movements employed by bees when dancing to indicate food sources, scented pheromones emitted by insects, and hand & finger signals employed by deaf persons. Every coding system as well as the corresponding set of meanings is always based on deliberately established conventions, and both the sender and the recipient should have a knowledge of these conventions. This knowledge is either transmitted directly (e g as input in electronic processing systems, or by inheritance in natural systems), or must be learned (e g mother tongue or any other language). The syntax of a language comprises the entire set of rules which determines the ways in which the single language elements can and should be combined.

Teleology/Teleonomy (Greek *telos* = purpose; *logos* = word, doctrine): Teleology is the doctrine that everything has a final purpose, especially living beings. As in the case of building and other structures, machines and appliances designed and built by humans, so teleology states that the purposefulness observed in all living beings and in the structure of the world, point to a purpose-giving Creator. This doctrine contradicts evolutionary thought which claims that development occurred without any purpose. *C S Pittendrigh* originally proposed that the concept of "purposefulness without purpose" should be termed teleonomy. This word is used for the evolutionary hypothesis of random chance. Purposeful processes are still recognised, but an Originator of purposes is excluded beforehand.

Transcendental (late Latin *transcendentia* = transgression): Crossing the boundary between this world and the next.

Trichotomy (late Greek *trichotomía* = division into thirds; *tricha* = threefold; *tome* = cut): Human beings are regarded as consisting of three parts, body, soul, and spirit (opposing view: → dichotomy). The Bible does not regard these three as separate realities, but as facets of one single person (e g 1 Thess 5:23).

Triplet (French *triplet*, Latin *triplus* = threefold): A DNA chain consists of a non-cyclic sequence of between one million and one thousand million nucleotides of which there are only four different ones (A = adenine, T = thymine, C = cytosine, G = guanine). Every three of these nucleotides (e g ACC, ATC, etc) form a triplet or codon which uniquely indicate (encode) one of the 20 amino acids. The triplets are the basic words used in genetic information (→ code).

Viroid (derived from virus; Latin *virus* = mucus, soft, poison): A complex aggregation of molecules; the simplest form of life; similar to a simple virus.

Zytoplasm (Greek *kytos* = sphericity, canopy): The components of a cell around the nucleus.

Werner Gitt

Questions
I have always wanted to ask

160 pages
DM 3,80
ISBN 3-89397-184-X

Everyone who starts to take interest in
the Christian faith is confronted by
numerous questions. For each person
searching for God, there is a remarkable
tendency to ask the same questions.

There was therefore a need to collect
these questions and to answer them
in a short but adequate form. All the
questions which have been dealt with in
this book have one thing in common –
they are genuine questions. It is not
a book of cross-section answers for
Christian insiders, but tries instead to
take each problem seriously, which
occupies the minds of those who are
doubting, questioning and searching.

It is not at all a collection of hair-
splitting theological or constructed
theoretical points, but instead it handles
basic questions which have been the
result of a series of lectures given by the
author of this book. Unusual questions
have also been dealt with.

On the following pages you will find an excerpt from the
book "Questions I have always wanted to ask".

2. Questions Concerning the Bible (QB)

The following set of questions which focuses on the validity and reliability of the Bible, is fundamental in nature. This is why only four questions are dealt with in this chapter. A very detailed Appendix – as befits the importance of this subject – has been added.

QB 1: *The Bible was recorded by people: does this not make everything relative? How can you say that it is from God and that everything is true?*

AB 1: We want to answer the question concerning scriptural truth by means of a specific example which has the advantage of being reconstructible mathematically. The Bible contains 6408 verses with prophetic statements of which 3268 have come to pass, while the remaining prophecies concern future events. No fulfilment of a prophecy differed from the way it was described to happen. This has not been equalled by any other book in world history. What we have here is a truth quota – also expressible in mathematical formulae – which has no equal anywhere else. We now want to ask: is it possible that so many prophecies came to pass by coincidence? i.e. can their fulfilment be explained without the intervention of God? In considering these questions, let us use a probability formula. In the calculation model below, two things have been ignored, namely that sometimes several verses in the Bible describe a single prophecy and, on the other hand, that one verse sometimes contains several prophecies. Similarly, the fact that some prophecies are mentioned several times is not included in the calculation. This simplification of the model is set off, however, by the following formulation for the basic probability.

If one assumes the very high basic probability of $p = 0{,}5$ for the *chance* fulfilment of a single prophecy, then the overall probability w for the 3268 prophecies which have come to pass already can be accurately calculated. This is $w = 2^{-3268} =$

$1{,}714 \cdot 10^{-984}$. The prophecies are such that the chances of their occurring as described can be formulated mathematically to be from 1:1000 to 1: several millions. With the formulation 1:2 (= 0,5) we would thus err on the safe side. To compare numbers for w let us look at several imaginary lottery systems. If the probability for a 'jackpot' in the commercial number lottery '6 in 49' ie 6 correct numbers in 49 blocks with consecutive numbering, is about 1:14 million, then let us ask: How many more blocks would we need to add on a second lottery ticket where 6 correct numbers were to be considered a 'jackpot' in order to attain that probability which would account for the chance fulfilment of 3268 prophecies? What would we estimate?

a) the size of a table tennis table?
   On an area of $A = 1{,}525 \times 2{,}74m = 4{,}1785m$, L would be 167 140 blocks of the size as seen on a common commercial lottery ticket.

b) the size of a soccer field?
   Where $A = 7350m$, L would be 459 375 000 blocks are possible.

c) or even the surface of the entire earth?
   If $A = 510$ million km, L would be $31{,}3653 \cdot 10^{18}$ blocks are possible, where 10^{18} would be a trillion or a million million million.

If one were to calculate the probabilities of having six correct numbers for L times numbered blocks, then the following values would be true for the above areas:

a) $w = 1 : 0{,}4 \cdot 10^{30}$ (or $2{,}5 \cdot 10^{-30}$)
b) $w = 1 : 1{,}3 \cdot 10^{49}$ (or $7{,}69 \cdot 10^{-50}$)
c) $w = 1 : 1{,}3 \cdot 10^{114}$ (or $7{,}69 \cdot 10^{-115}$)

The numbers for w show that the comparisons a) through c) are totally inadequate. The mathematical result for the number of blocks is absolutely breathtaking. In order to compare the amounts adequately we would need to draw on the total number of atoms in the universe and this, being 10^{80}, is in itself no longer imaginable. It is a 1 with 80 zeros or the figure 10 million millions multiplied 8 times by itself. To reach the calculated trans-astronomical figure of $2,74 \cdot 10^{164}$ blocks of that super lottery ticket, one would have to draw a comparison which exceeds our imagination even further: If one imagines as many universes of the same size as our universe has atoms, then the total number of atoms of all of these imaginary universes would still be smaller by a factor of 27 4000 than the required lottery ticket should have blocks [G1, 139].

After the above considerations, we can come to one conclusion only: the prophecies are divine, their origin cannot be human. In this way, the calculation leads us to a result which Jesus compresses to the brief formula (often incorrectly described as High Priest prayer, although it does not involve a High Priest service, ie the atonement of the nation's sins) "Your word is truth" (John 17:17). The Scriptures can therefore not be of human origin, on the contrary: "All Scripture is God-breathed" (2 Tim. 3:16). God used selected people to whom He gave important information so that they – without excluding their personality, their nature and their emotions – could record these for us. Additional information concerning this question can be found in three sub-chapters in the Appendix Fundamental Principles of the Bible: I.1 Its origin I.2 Its truth content I.3 Testing biblical truths

QB 2: *How can I find out whether the Bible is true?*

AB 2: A panel cannot decide whether a mathematically formulated, physical process or a particular chemical reaction given specific conditions will occur or not, but an experiment will prove or disprove it. In contrast to all other writings of ideologies and religions, the Bible names methods of proving its truth empirically. Those whose questions are not only of a philosophical nature, but are really searching for an answer are invited to take part in an experiment for which God Himself will vouch.

"Do not let this Book of the Law depart from your mouth; meditate on it day and night, so that you may be careful to do everything written in it" (Josh. 1:8).

This experiment thus consists of three steps:

1. *Get to know the specifications of the experiment:* First of all we need to know the contents of the Bible by reading it diligently.

2. *Implementing the experiment:* Secondly, instructions that have been understood, are to be put into practice.

3. *Testing of the experimental data:* Everybody desires a successful life in the areas of marriage and family, profession and leisure time. The questions put to councillors in the popular press provide sufficient evidence. No psychological marriage counsellor, no industrial manager and no political consultant has an ultimate recipe for success up his sleeve. Only Scripture promises success and wise actions if the above conditions are met.

Those that carry out this experiment, always arrive at a positive conclusion. There is neither loss nor risk, nor are any stakes lost as is the case for a lottery or loss of interest for credit. If you challenge the Bible, you are dealing with God and your gain will be enormous (Further possibilities for testing are included in the Appendix Annotations to the Bible, Part I2. The biblical truths).

QB 3: *In what respects does the Bible differ from other books of world literature?*

AB 3: The Bible differs fundamentally in several respects from other books of world literature as it represents a unique, singular and incomparable work:

1. *Despite having been written over a span of 1000 years, Scripture possesses a unique continuity:* The Bible was written by approximately 45 writers of different backgrounds and professions. Among the writers are for example the university graduate Moses, the military commander-in-chief Joshua, the prime minister Daniel, the cupbearer Nehemiah, King David, the shepherd Amos, the fisherman Peter, the customs officer Matthew, the doctor Luke and the tent maker Paul. The sections of the Bible were written in unusual places such as the desert (Moses), the jail (Jeremiah), the palace (Daniel), on tour (Luke) or in exile (John) and marked by every imaginable emotion of the writers such as joy and love, fear and anxiety, suffering and despair. Despite the time span of 60 generations which is found nowhere else and the different social levels of its authors, the Bible is characterized by uniformity and harmony in all subject matters. The writers deal with hundreds of topics with obvious harmony and consistency. Experience has shown that if men from such distant eras and with such divergent personalities were to deal with such a spectrum of topics without the intervention of God, no such unity could be expected. In particular, God and His plan to rescue mankind from the path of self- destruction runs through the Bible like a scarlet thread.

2. *Scripture is made up of a wide scope of literary genres not to be found in any other book* (see Principle P58 in Appendix, Part I). On the other hand, other genres which do not represent truth such as fairy tales, legends and sagas are excluded. Nor do we find exaggerations or understatements as we know them from satires, glosses, epics or comedies.

3. *The Bible is characterized by remarkable diversity.* It is a book on faith, law and history all at the same time. It supplies the foundations for numerous disciplines and contains thousands of guidelines concerning many day-to-day situations. It is the best counsel for marriages and describes how we should interact with parents and children, friends and enemies, neighbours and relatives, strangers, guests and fellow-believers (for details see question QL 3). It deals with the origin of this world and of all life, the nature of death and the end of the world. It shows us the nature of God, the Father, His Son Jesus Christ and the workings of the Holy Spirit.

4. *The Bible is the only book which contains absolutely trustworthy prophecies.* As they are of divine origin (1 Sam 9:9; 2 Sam 24:11; 2 Peter 1:20-21) they cannot be found in any other book of world literature (neither in the Qur'an nor in the records of the French occultist Nostradamus). The time lapse between actual writing and its fulfilment is so great that not even the most severe critic could claim that the prophecies had only been given after the events had already taken place (for details see [G1 118-148]).

5. *The time background for biblical testimony has no equal anywhere:* The Bible in its statements extends from the point of origin of the physical time axis (creation) to its conclusion (Rev. 20:6b). No other book records with any certainty the beginnings of time nor can it describe the end of the time axis with any accuracy. Furthermore, the Bible talks about eternity, that reality in which our restrictive temporal laws are no longer valid.

6. *No assertion of the Bible has yet been proved incorrect.* No scientific references in the Bible have ever been revised due to research results. On the contrary, there are numerous examples to prove that scientific descriptions in the Bible were only proved correct by research many centuries later (eg the number of stars [G1, 58-59, shape of the earth [G1, 59-60]).

7. *No other book describes man as realistically as does the Bible.* There are no comic exaggerations, no touched-up biographies and no glorified heroism, which hides or veils the negative aspects of man. This is why, for instance, the sins of the patriarchs in the Bible (Gen. 12:11-13), the adultery of David (2 Sam. 11) and the disorder in the churches (1 Cor. 1:11; 2 Cor. 2:1-4) are not omitted.

8. *The Bible mentions future events which no man with the knowledge available at that time could have imagined* (eg space labs, orbit stations: Obadiah 4) and includes situations in its teaching which occurred only many centuries later (such as drug abuse, 2 Cor. 6:16-17; gene technology: see question QL 10).